Standard Specification for Water and Sewerage Schemes

Third Edition

SADWSS
SCOTTISH ASSOCIATION OF DIRECTORS
OF WATER AND SEWERAGE SERVICES

STANDARD SPECIFICATION FOR WATER

AND SEWERAGE SCHEMES

PUBLISHED BY THE WATER RESEARCH CENTRE (1989) PLC,
HENLEY ROAD, MEDMENHAM,
PO BOX 16, MARLOW, BUCKS. SL7 2HD.
ON BEHALF OF SADWSS

THE SPECIFICATION STARTS AT SERIES 100 AND FINISHES AT THE END OF SERIES 1500

FOREWORD - THIRD EDITION

The Standard Specification for Water and Sewerage Schemes was first published in 1973 and was prepared under the auspices of the Scottish Development Department. A revision was published in 1979.

The document has been widely used by local authorities, government departments, consulting engineers and others in Scotland and Northern Ireland over the years for a range of contracts of varying sizes.

In late 1986, the Scottish Association of Directors of Water and Sewerage Services (SADWASS) felt there was a need for a further revision of the document and with the agreement of the Scottish Development Department set up a Working Party with representatives from each regional water and sewerage authority. The Working Party was augmented with representatives from the Department of the Environment for Northern Ireland, the Association of Consulting Engineers and the Federation of Civil Engineering Contractors. The Scottish Development Department and the Water Research Centre in Scotland provided representatives initially to provide advice but who later provided sterling services during editing of the document.

Initially the Working Party gave consideration to the form of the revised document with much discussion as to whether the document should be of a method or performance specification. A decision was however taken to keep the previous form of specification which had been well tried and met the needs of most authorities for the majority of their contracts. Notwithstanding it was agreed to make fairly radical changes if felt necessary. As a result certain sections of the previous document have been eliminated or consolidated with other sections and new sections such as those of Tunnelling and Pipejacking, Metal Structures, Cladding and Painting and Reconditioning of Mains and Sewer Renovation were incorporated.

It is anticipated that the Working Party may meet from time to time in the future to consider amendments to this Third Edition. Any user who has any suggestion for amendment to the Specification should contact any Director of Water and Sewerage in Scotland who will forward the suggested amendment to the Working Party Chairman.

J. IVISON
Chairman

THE THIRD EDITION OF THE SPECIFICATION WAS PREPARED UNDER THE AUSPICES OF THE SCOTTISH ASSOCIATION OF DIRECTORS OF WATER AND SEWERAGE SERVICES BY A WORKING PARTY OF CIVIL ENGINEERS REPRESENTATIVE OF THE FOLLOWING BODIES.

SCOTTISH ASSOCIATION OF DIRECTORS OF WATER AND SEWERAGE SERVICES
ASSOCIATION OF CONSULTING ENGINEERS
THE FEDERATION OF CIVIL ENGINEERING CONTRACTORS
DEPARTMENT OF THE ENVIRONMENT FOR NORTHERN IRELAND
SCOTTISH DEVELOPMENT DEPARTMENT
WATER RESEARCH CENTRE PLC

THE WORKING PARTY COMPRISED THE FOLLOWING:

J. IVISON (CHAIRMAN) (UNTIL 31 DECEMBER 1989)

C.E. SCHOOLING (CHAIRMAN)

A. ANDERSON (TECHNICAL SECRETARY)

P.M. BARR

D.H. BLAIR

G. BREWSTER

D.J. DODDS

T.H. DOUGLAS

I.D. ISAAC

D. GALLACHER

W.F. GOW

J.M. GREEN

R.B. HEGGIE

C. SHEPHERD

P.H. SMITH

T.H. STEWART

P.H. TAYLOR

W.M. WILSON

R. FELLOWS

A. DAVIDSON (ASSISTANT TECHNICAL SECRETARY)

J. McFADZEAN (ASSISTANT TECHNICAL SECRETARY)

COMPLIANCE WITH BRITISH STANDARDS

1.   British Standards and other documents referred to in the Contract shall be deemed to be those current 42 days prior to the date for return of Tenders.

2.   Where an appropriate British Standard or equivalent exists the materials and products incorporated in the works should comply with its relevant provisions. They should also be Kitemarked where appropriate, though the mark of conformity of any other third party certification body accredited by the National Accreditation Council for Certification Bodies or equivalent is an acceptable alternative.

3.   Any problems or complaints experienced with Kitemark certified products should be brought to the attention of the Head of Department (Building and Construction) of B.S.I. Similarly in respect of products required to comply with a Water Industry specification, any problem or complaint should be brought to the attention of the Manager of the Water Industry Certification Scheme. The manager of any other appropriate certification body should be approached in respect of any complaint relative to a product supplied to an equivalent specification. A sample of the questionnaire to be used is given in Appendix 1. A copy of each completed questionnaire should be sent to the head office of the relevant water authority, marked for the attention of its BSI Liaison Officer. This procedure is not intended to affect the provisions of the Contract.

General Notes

1.   The specification is intended for use in conjunction with the Fifth Edition of the ICE Conditions of Contract and the Civil Engineering Standard Method of Measurement (CESMM).

2.   There is no reference in the Specification either to the method of assessing payment or to whether the Employer or the Contractor should bear specific costs; these matters are left for inclusion in the Bill of Quantities and its Preamble.

4.   Notes for Guidance are included after the main text and are designed primarily to assist those preparing contract documents, but do not form part of the specification.

Feedback Arrangements

Any suggestion for amendment of the Specification should be sent to any Director of Water and Sewerage in Scotland.

Definitions

In the Specification the following words and expressions shall have the meanings hereby assigned to them except where the context otherwise requires:

    i   'Approved' means approved by the Engineer
    ii   'Approved in Writing' means approved by the Engineer in writing
    iii   'Directed' means directed by the Engineer
    iv   'Permitted means permitted by the Engineer
    v   The following words shall have the meanings ascribed to them in Clause 1 Definitions of the Conditions of Contract
'Contract', 'Engineer', 'Engineer's Representative', 'Contractor', 'Employer', 'Works', 'Permanent Works' and 'Site'.

    vi   'Period of Execution of the Works' means that period calculated from the Date for Commencement as notified by the Engineer in writing until the date stated on the Certificate of Completion.

    vii   'Final Completion' means the date of the issue of the Maintenance Certificate.

CONTENTS

CONTENTS

CONTENTS

CONTENTS

CONTENTS

CONTENTS

CONTENTS

Site Clearance, Access and General

101. Accommodation for the Engineer

1. The Contractor shall provide heat, light, clean and maintain, until completion of the Works and remove thereafter, or when directed, accommodation as *required by the Contract* for the sole use of the Engineer and his staff. The accommodation shall be erected, furnished, fully equipped and serviced as *required by the Contract* and ready for occupation within 14 days from the date for commencement of the Works. Unless otherwise *required by the Contract*, the accommodation shall be located on a site to be obtained by the Contractor and approved by the Engineer.

2. The Contractor shall supply for the period of execution of the Works testing equipment as *required by the Contract* for the use of the Engineer and his staff. The equipment shall be set up in a testing laboratory as *required by the Contract* and shall be kept in accurate working order throughout the period of execution of the Works.

3. The Contractor shall provide for the period of execution of the Works a telephone and extensions, as *required by the Contract*, for the exclusive use of the Engineer and his staff. It shall have an independent connection to the national telephone system with privacy of conversation and shall be kept in working order throughout the period of execution of the Works.

4. The Contractor shall supply for the period of execution of the Works, surveying equipment as *required by the Contract* for the exclusive use of the Engineer and his staff and shall maintain it in accurate working order throughout the period of execution of the Works.

102. Work on Roads

1. Throughout the execution and maintenance of the Works, the Contractor shall cooperate with the Highway and Police Authorities, or landowner, concerning works affecting any road. The Contractor shall inform the Engineer of any requirements of, or arrangements made with, the Highway and Police Authorities or landowner. Before any work affecting the use of any road, public or private, is commenced, the Contractor's proposed method of working shall be approved in writing.

103. Traffic Requirements

1. The Contractor shall provide all items and take such measures as may be necessary to comply with the relevant provisions of the Traffic Safety Measures for Road Works as contained in Chapter 8 of the Traffic Signs Manual, published by Her Majesty's Stationery Office, or where appropriate signing shall comply with the relevant provisions of Advice Note TA/6/80: 'Traffic signs and safety measures for minor works on minor roads', published by the Department of Transport as an addendum to Chapter 8.

2. The Contractor shall keep clean and legible at all times all traffic signs, road markings, lamps, barriers and traffic control signals and he shall position, reposition, cover or remove them as necessitated by the progress of the Works.

3. The Contractor shall take every precaution to prevent dirt and mud or other material being dropped or spread by traffic from the Works on roads and paths.
The Contractor shall also clean roads and paths of any dirt and mud which is unavoidably spilled by traffic travelling to and from or on the Site in connection with the Works. The Contractor may be directed to carry out such cleaning work outwith normal working hours to minimise traffic disruption.

4. The Contractor shall construct temporary diversion ways wherever the Works will interfere with existing public or private roads or other ways over which there is a public or private right of way for any traffic. Nevertheless, where approved, the Contractor may make arrangements for temporary closure of such public or private road or right of way.
The standard of construction and lighting shall be suitable in all respects for the class or classes of traffic using the existing way and the width of any diversion shall not be less than that of the existing way unless otherwise *required by the Contract*.

104. Privately Owned and Public Utility Services

1.   The positions of public utility and other services close to the Works are indicated in the contract as far as they are believed to exist, but no warranty is given as to the accuracy or completeness of this information.

2.   The Contractor shall inform the Engineer and the owner of the service of his intention and programme at least 21 days before starting work in the vicinity of any service, and shall request the appropriate statutory authority or owner to indicate on the ground the locations of all public utility services, service connections, road drainage and other underground services prior to the commencement of work. The Contractor shall then carry out excavations by hand to determine the exact locations and depths of all underground services in advance of the main excavation work.

3.   Where any portion of the Works is close to, across, or under any existing service, the Contractor shall take the necessary steps to protect the service and to ensure its uninterrupted operation. On completion of work in their vicinity services shall be properly bedded and backfilled in accordance with the requirements of the owner. Should any damage be discovered the Contractor shall at once notify the Engineer and the statutory authority or owner, and the Contractor shall afford every facility for the repair or replacement of the service.

105. Site Clearance

1.   The Contractor shall demolish, break up and remove buildings, structures and superficial obstructions on the Site in the way of or otherwise affected by the Permanent Works. Bushes, undergrowth or small trees the trunks of which are less than 500 mm in girth at 1 m above ground level, tree stumps less than 150 mm dia. and hedges shall be uprooted and disposed of as approved.

2.   Underground structures and chambers being superseded by the Works shall be demolished to a depth not less than 600 mm below finished ground level unless otherwise *required by the Contract*. They shall be properly cleaned out, have their floors punctured so that they do not retain water, and be filled in accordance with Clause 209.

106. Existing Trees, Stumps and Roots

1.   Where *required by the Contract*, trees shall be uprooted or cut down as near to ground level as possible. All felled timber shall be disposed of as *required by the Contract*.

2.   Stumps and tree roots shall, unless otherwise directed, be grubbed up and disposed of by the Contractor as approved. Holes left by the stumps or roots shall within one week be backfilled in accordance with Clause 209.

3.   Prior to any tree felling work being started, trees to be felled shall be surveyed, marked, measured and recorded by the Engineer and the Contractor.

4.   The Contractor shall take all reasonable steps to ensure that in carrying out his operations no damage is caused to any trees. No excavation shall be carried out under the branch spread except where *required by the Contract*. All such excavation shall be carried out by hand around main roots and shall remain open for the shortest possible time before being backfilled. No tree root in excess of 50 mm dia. shall be cut, and all cuts and snicks or roots shall be painted over with approved tree paint. Backfilling shall be carefully rammed around roots to eliminate voids.

107. Tidiness of Site

1.   The Contractor shall be responsible for the proper upkeep and maintenance of the Site and the Works and shall remove from the Site rubbish and other waste as it accumulates. Materials and equipment shall be positioned, stored and stacked in an orderly manner.

108. Working Area

1. The Contractor shall for the purposes of the Contract have free and temporary use of working areas and accesses thereto as *required by the Contract*. The Contractor shall be responsible for making up and maintaining in suitable condition for his construction traffic all such accesses including, where required, the provision of temporary bridges and adequate fencing. The Contractor shall carry out reinstatement in designated areas as *required by the Contract* immediately on completion of the works in each area.

2. Unless otherwise *required by the Contract*, no provision will be made by the Employer for areas to be occupied by the Contractor's offices, stores, plant, additional working areas and the like. The Contractor shall arrange for the use of such areas and any further working areas or accesses required during the progress of the Works.

3. Where the Works are in close proximity to buildings, walls or other existing structures, the Contractor shall take adequate measures to prevent any damage to such structures. In addition before commencing work the Contractor shall submit details in writing to the Engineer of his proposed method of carrying out these measures and shall not commence operations until these are approved in writing.

4. Where *required by the Contract*, the working areas and accesses shall be fenced immediately on entry in accordance with Series 800 of this Specification.

109. Storage of Explosives and Other Dangerous Substances

1. No explosive or other dangerous substance shall be brought onto the Site or used for any purpose unless previously approved in writing.

2. The location of each explosives magazine and store of any other dangerous substance on the Site shall be approved in writing.

3. The storage of explosives shall be in accordance with the provisions of BS 5607.

4. The Contractor shall provide to the Engineer in writing clear evidence that the proposed location, type and security arrangements of explosives magazines and of stores of other dangerous or flammable materials or gases comply with all statutory requirements and regulations.

110. Pollution of Watercourses

1. During the period of execution of the Works, the Contractor shall take all necessary precautions to prevent the pollution or silting of beaches, rivers, streams, lochs, watercourses, reservoir catchment areas, surface water drains or the surface of the ground by poisonous, noxious or polluting matter arising from his operations, and shall provide any settling ponds or purifying equipment necessary to comply with the requirements of the appropriate River Purification Authority.

111. Contamination of Water Supplies

1. If *required by the Contract*, before any person is engaged on work on the Site he shall be notified of the need for personal hygiene and the dangers of contamination, shall complete a medical questionnaire provided by the Employer and, where there is a need, shall be tested to indicate that he is not a carrier of typhoid or other waterborne disease. The Contractor shall notify the Engineer of any person who has been certified by a doctor as suffering from an illness associated with the looseness of the bowels, and no such person shall be employed on such work until the Employer's medical adviser is satisfied that it is safe.

12

Excavation, Backfilling and Restoration

201. General

1. The Contractor shall carry out his operations in such a manner as to avoid damage to, or deterioration of, the Final Surfaces of excavations.

2. Excavations shall be taken out to the least dimensions required to accommodate the several parts of the Permanent Works and shall provide any working space necessary for their execution.

3. The sides of the excavations shall be adequately supported at all times and, except where *required or permitted under the Contract*, shall not be battered. No timber or other supports shall be left in the excavations unless approved.

4. No excavated material other than that surplus to the requirements of the Works shall be removed from the Site, unless *required by the Contract* or approved. Should the Contractor be permitted to remove suitable material from the Site to suit his operational procedure, he shall make good any consequent deficit of filling arising therefrom. Suitable material shall comprise all that which is acceptable in accordance with the Contract for use in the Permanent Works.

5. Suitable material and topsoil surplus to the requirements of the Works and all unsuitable material from general excavations shall be disposed of in spoil tips off Site provided by the Contractor.

202. Topsoil

1. Topsoil shall mean the top layer of soil that can support vegetation and shall include all turf which is not required for relaying or not acceptable for turfing under Clause 217.

2. Topsoil shall be removed from the areas *required by the Contract* and, where required for re-use, shall be stockpiled separately. Before removing topsoil the Contractor shall record and agree with the Engineer ground levels and depths of topsoil.

3. The height of topsoil stockpiles shall not exceed 2 m. Topsoil shall not be unnecessarily trafficked before stripping, when in stockpile and after spreading.

203. Dealing with Water

1. The Contractor shall provide, maintain and operate pumping plant, and construct such grips, drains, sumps and catchwaters as may be necessary to remove water from the excavations or to prevent its entrance thereto. Water in the excavations shall be dealt with in such manner as will protect the surfaces on or against which foundations or other work will be constructed from any deterioration from their natural condition, or from such condition as improved by work executed under the Contract.

2. Any drainage sumps required shall, where practicable, be sited outside the area excavated for the Permanent Works. All drainage sumps shall be refilled with concrete Grade C15 or other approved material to the level of the underside of the adjacent Permanent Works.

3. The Contractor shall prevent any adjacent ground from being adversely affected by loss of fines through dewatering.

4. Water from excavations shall be discharged in an approved manner.

204. Excavations in Rock

1. The method of excavation in rock shall prevent damage to existing structures and to the Works.

205. Blasting

1. Blasting shall be carried out only with prior written approval and then only by methods, in places and at such times as permitted. Such approval shall not relieve the Contractor of his

responsibility for damage or accidents caused to properties, workmen or third parties as a result of his operations.

2.   The Contractor shall comply with BS 5607.

3.   The Contractor shall demonstrate, by means of site trials and vibration regression curves derived therefrom that the proposed blasting methods will comply with the peak particle vibration and noise criteria *required by the Contract*.

4.   The Contractor shall comply with BS 6657 in respect of the use of electrical detonators in the vicinity of static and mobile radio transmitters, including normal radio and television broadcasting stations and radar units associated with aircraft movements.

5.   Explosives shall not be brought onto the Site unless approved in writing. The location of stores or registered premises for explosives shall be as approved.

6.   Blasting operations shall be carried out only by properly licensed and certificated shotfirers.

7.   The minimum amount of explosives required to achieve the desired result shall be used. Precautions shall be taken to prevent damage by flying rock.

206.   Preparation of Final Surface
1.   When approaching the Final Surface in material other than rock, the final trimming for foundations or blinding concrete shall not take place until placing of concrete is about to commence.

2.   When approaching the Final Surface in rock, the Contractor may be directed to continue excavating without the use of explosives or with limited use thereof by shallow holes and light charges. The final trimming to the Final Surface shall be executed without explosives by approved hand tools.

3.   All loose and soft material, and water shall be removed from the rock surface before placing concrete and the rock surfaces shall be maintained free of water during concreting.

207.   Excess Excavation
1.   Excavations in excess of that *required by the Contract* shall be filled with such materials and in such manner as directed.

208.   Unsuitable Ground
1.   If the Contractor encounters ground in the Final Surface which he considers to be unsuitable, or if the Final Surface is damaged or allowed to deteriorate, the Engineer shall be immediately informed. The Contractor shall excavate and remove to tip all unsuitable material encountered at the Final Surface and shall refill the additional excavation with materials and in the manner as *required by the Contract*. The Contractor shall not excavate below the levels *required by the Contract* without approval. Unsuitable material shall mean other than suitable material and shall include:-

   (a)   material from swamps, marshes or bogs,

   (b)   peat, logs, stumps and perishable material,

   (c)   material susceptible to spontaneous combustion,

   (d)   material in a frozen condition or which after being frozen is not approved for use,

   (e)   clay of liquid limit exceeding 90 or plasticity index exceeding 65 and

   (f)   materials having a moisture content greater than the maximum *required by the Contract*.

209. Backfilling; General

1.   Backfilling shall be undertaken as soon as practicable after the specified operations preceding it, including water testing of structures, have been completed. Backfilling shall not be commenced until the works to be covered have been completed to the extent *required by the Contract* and have achieved a strength sufficient to withstand all loading imposed thereon.

2.   Filling material to excavations not situated in highways or prospective highways shall consist of selected fill deposited in layers and compacted to the requirements of Clause 212 or 214 as appropriate. Selected fill, whether from locally excavated material or imported, shall consist of uniform, readily compactible material, and shall not contain materials deemed unsuitable as specified in Clause 208.1. The size of clay lumps and stones in the selected fill shall not exceed two thirds of the compacted layer thickness.

3.   Where the excavations have been supported and the supports are to be removed, these shall be withdrawn progressively as backfilling proceeds in such a manner as to minimise the danger of collapse. All voids behind the supports shall be filled and compacted.

210. Forming of Embankments and Other Areas of Fill; General

1.   Topsoil and unsuitable foundation material shall be removed from the areas on which embankments and other areas of fill are to be constructed unless *required by the Contract*.

2.   Where an embankment is to be placed on sloping ground, the surface shall be benched in steps as *required by the Contract*.

3.   Drainage and preparation work on the sites of embankments and other areas of fill shall be approved before embankment placing commences.

4.   Embankments and other areas of fill shall be formed to allow as much time as possible for settlement to take place before paths, drains or other works are laid over them.

5.   During the construction of embankments and other areas of fill the Contractor shall direct constructional traffic uniformly over their full width, to prevent damage to compacted layers.

211. Materials

1.   Embankment and other areas of fill shall be formed of suitable materials and shall not contain materials deemed unsuitable as specified in Clause 208.1.

2.   If the material deposited as fill subsequently reaches a condition such that it cannot be compacted as *required by the Contract* the Contractor shall either:-

   (a)   remove the material and replace it with suitable material, or

   (b)   make good the material by mechanical or chemical means, or

   (c)   cease work on the material until its physical condition is such that it can be compacted as *required by the Contract*.

3.   Isolated stones may be incorporated in embankments and areas of fill provided they do not exceed two thirds the layer thickness and that the specified compaction requirements are met.

4.   Material used in rockfill embankments shall be of such size that it can be deposited in horizontal layers not exceeding 450 mm loose depth. Material shall be spread and levelled over the full width of the embankment and compacted in accordance with Clause 212. Each layer shall consist of reasonably graded rock and all surface voids shall be filled with broken fragments before the next layer is placed. The top surface and side slopes of embankments so formed shall be thoroughly blinded with approved fine graded material to seal the surface. Such material may, on side slopes and verges, be topsoil as defined in Clause 202.1.

212. Compaction of Embankments and Other Areas of Fill

1.   All materials used in embankments and other areas of fill shall be compacted as soon as practicable after deposition. Compaction shall be carried out in accordance with Table 200A, unless a variation thereof is approved.

2.   Variations from the methods given in Table 200A or the use of plant not included therein, will not be approved unless the Contractor demonstrates by site trials that an equivalent state of compaction can be achieved. The procedure to be adopted for site trials shall be as approved.

3.   The Engineer may at any time carry out comparative field density tests determined in accordance with BS 1377 test No. 15 on material which he considers has been inadequately compacted. If the test results, when compared with the results of similar tests made on adjacent approved work in similar materials carried out in accordance with Table 200A, show the state of compaction to be inadequate the Contractor shall carry out such further work as may be directed.

4.   Each layer in rockfill embankments shall be spread and levelled in accordance with Clause 211.4 and compacted by not less than 12 passes of a towed vibratory roller with a static mass per metre width of roll of not less than 1800 kg or other approved plant. Where rock is used as general fill and has the properties of rockfill it shall be spread and compacted as for rockfill in embankments. Where rock is used as general fill and contains or is mixed with sufficient soft material for satisfactory compaction to the requirements of Table 200A, for well graded granular soil, the fill shall be compacted to the latter requirements.

5.   When materials of widely divergent characteristics are used in embankments and fill areas they shall be spread and compacted in separate clearly defined areas in such a manner as to comply with the requirements of Table 200A.

6.   If more than one class of material is being used in such a way that it is not practicable to define the areas in which each class occurs, the compaction method shall be that appropriate to the material which requires the greatest compactive effort.

7.   Definitions and requirements associated with Table 200A:-

(a)   The depth of compacted layer is the height by which an embankment is raised by each successive compacted layer.

(b)   Number of passes is the number of times that each point on the surface of the layer being compacted has been traversed by the item of compaction plant.

(c)   The mass per metre width of roll is the total mass on the roll divided by the total roll width. Where a smooth wheeled roller has more than one axle the machine will be assessed on the basis of the axle giving the highest value of mass per metre width.

(d)   Vibratory rollers are self-propelled or towed rollers having means of applying mechanical vibration to one or more rolls.

(i)   The requirements for vibratory rollers are based on the use of the lowest gear on a self-propelled machine and a towing speed of 30 to 40 m per minute for a towed machine. If higher gears or speeds are used an increased number of passes shall be provided in proportion to the increase in speed of travel.

(ii)   Vibratory rollers operating without their vibration mechanism in use will be classified as smooth wheeled rollers.

(iii)   Vibratory rollers shall be operated only at the frequency of vibration recommended by the manufacturers.

(e)   Vibrating plate compactors are machines having a baseplate to which is attached a source of vibration.

(i)   The mass per unit area of baseplate of a vibrating plate compactor is calculated by dividing the total mass of the machine in its working condition by its area in contact with compacted soil.

TABLE 200A Compaction Requirements

Type of compaction plant	Category	Cohesive soil		Well-graded granular and dry cohesive soils		Uniformly-graded materials	
		Maximum depth of compacted layer mm	Minimum No. of passes	Maximum depth of compacted layer mm	Minimum No. of passes	Maximum depth of compacted layer mm	Minimum No. of passes
Smooth wheeled roller	Mass per metre width						
	2,100-2,700 kg	125	8	125	10	125	10*
	2,701-5,400 kg	125	8	125	8	125	8*
	Over 5,400 kg	150	4	150	8	Unsuitable	Unsuitable
Vibratory roller	Mass per metre width						
	270- 450 kg	Unsuitable	Unsuitable	75	16	150	16
	451- 700 kg	Unsuitable	Unsuitable	75	12	150	12
	701-1,300 kg	100	12	125	12	150	6
	1,301-1,800 kg	125	8	150	8	200	10*
Vibrating-plate compactor	Mass per unit area of base-plate						
	880-1,100 kg	Unsuitable	Unsuitable	Unsuitable	Unsuitable	75	6
	1,101-1,200 kg	Unsuitable	Unsuitable	75	10	100	6
	1,201-1,400 kg	Unsuitable	Unsuitable	75	6	150	6
	1,401-1,800 kg	100	6	125	6	150	4
	1,801-2,100 kg	100	6	150	5	200	4
	Over 2,100 kg	200	6	200	5	250	4
Vibro-tamper	Mass Kilogramme						
	50-65	100	3	100	3	150	3
	65-75	125	3	125	3	200	3
	More than 75	200	3	150	3	220	3
Power rammer	Mass Kilogramme						
	100-500	150	4	150	6	Unsuitable	Unsuitable
	More than 500	270	8	275	12	Unsuitable	Unsuitable

Notes for Table 200A

For the purpose of Table 200A materials are grouped as follows:-

(a) Cohesive soil includes clays and marls with up to 20 per cent of gravel and having a moisture content not less than the value of the plastic limit, determined in accordance with BS 1377 test No. 3, minus 4 and also chalk having a saturation moisture content of 20 per cent or greater.

(b) Well graded granular and dry cohesive soils include clays and marls containing more than 20 per cent of gravel and or having a moisture content less than the value of the plastic limit, determined in accordance with BS 1377 test No. 3, minus 4, well graded sands and gravels with a uniformity coefficient exceeding 10, chalk having a saturation moisture content within the range 15 to 20 per cent and all shales and clinker ash.

(c) Uniformly-graded material includes sands and gravels with a uniformity coefficient of 10 or less, and all silts and pulverised fuel ashes. Any soil containing 80 per cent or more of material in the particle size range 0.06 to 0.002 mm will be regarded as silt for this purpose.

(ii) Vibrating plate compactors shall be operated at the frequency of vibration recommended by the manufacturers. They shall be operated at travelling speeds of not more than 15 m per minute.

(f) Vibro tampers are machines in which an engine driven reciprocating mechanism acts on a spring system, through which oscillations are set up in a baseplate.

(g) Power rammers are machines which are actuated by explosions in an internal combustion cylinder, each explosion being controlled manually by the operator. Each strike of the power rammer shall be considered as one pass.

(h) For items marked * in Table 200A the rollers shall be towed by track laying tractors. Self-propelled rollers are unsuitable.

213. Embankments and Other Areas of Fill to be kept Free from Water

1. During construction water shed on to the embankments and other areas of fill or completed formation of access roads, or which enters such works from any source, shall be rapidly dispersed and where practicable shall be discharged into the permanent outfall for the pipe drainage systems. Adequate means for trapping silt shall be provided on temporary systems discharging into permanent drainage systems.

2. Temporary watercourses, ditches, drains, pumping or other means of maintaining earthworks free from water shall be provided. Earthwork surfaces shall have sufficient crossfall and, where practicable, a sufficient longitudinal gradient to enable them to shed water and prevent ponding.

214. Filling Against Structures

1. In forming embankments or other areas of fill against structures precautions shall be taken to ensure that no damage is caused by tipping or compacting plant. Where special forms of compaction adjacent to structures are *required by the Contract*, filling may proceed over widths less than the full width of the embankment or other fill area and in steps not exceeding the depth of one layer above the adjoining area of fill. In rockfill embankments the rocks shall be packed carefully for such distance from the structure as is *required by the Contract*.

2. Backfilling around tanks and other structures shall be undertaken in such a manner as to avoid uneven loading.

215. Filling on Roofs

1. Fill on roofs of tanks and underground chambers shall be placed in an approved manner. Compaction of fill shall be effected as *required by the Contract* or as directed. No materials shall be stored on the roofs of tanks and underground chambers without written approval.

216. Restoration; Land Drains

1. The positions of all land drains intercepted or disturbed shall be prominently marked. The Contractor shall record these positions, depths, pipe diameters and the types of construction, and a copy of these records shall be given to the Engineer. The Contractor shall ensure that markers are not disturbed during the progress of the Works.

2. Prior to the permanent reinstatement of land drainage the ends of existing drains, where intercepted by excavations, shall be cleared and facilities afforded to the Engineer and the landowner or occupier to inspect them and determine the extent of replacement that may be necessary.

3. The backfill of intercepting excavations shall be compacted to give a firm bearing immediately before replacement pipes are laid, and shall be brought up to the level of the underside of the land drains or of any support to be provided.

4. The affected land drains shall be cut back into firm ground until a section is exposed which is unaffected by the Works.

5.   Replacement pipes or support beams, where they are required, shall bear on undisturbed ground for at least 500 mm at each end. The replacement pipes shall be of the same internal diameter as the sections of drain which they replace, and shall be properly connected at each end.

6.   Records shall be kept of all drainage system reinstatement work carried out, and a copy shall be given to the Engineer. The record shall include the direction of the flow and alignment of the drain in relation to the excavation.

217.   Soiling, Grassing and Turfing
1.   The Contractor shall break up and cultivate the surface of all land to be soiled and grassed and all land to be reinstated outwith the Permanent Works to a depth of not less than 300 mm. Reinstatement of land shall include replacing topsoil and restoring the land as closely as possible to its original condition.

2.   The areas to be grassed shall be covered with topsoil which shall be reduced to a fine tilth free from stones and other debris with any dimension greater than 50 mm. The topsoil shall be lightly compacted.

3.   Fertilisers or herbicides shall not be used unless they are of a type approved in writing. Fertiliser and lime on a topsoil shall be evenly distributed using the mixtures and at the rate of application *required by the Contract*.

4.   Seed shall be sown at the proper season paying due regard to the weather conditions and all reasonable measures shall be taken to promote its growth. Grass seed shall be evenly distributed at the rate of application *required by the Contract*.

5.   Where hydraulic mulch seeding is specified, the proprietary process shall be approved and shall contain types and quantities of seed, mulch material, fertiliser and other necessary additives to produce a covering sward on subsoil.

6.   Turfing shall be carried out on topsoil using turfs to BS 3969. Suitable turf which is to be stripped from within the Site shall be used wherever possible. Turfing shall be undertaken with clean strong turfs well bonded and lightly beaten and on side slopes shall be laid diagonally. Unless directed all turfs shall be used within one week of cutting during the period 1 April to 31 August or at other times within two weeks of cutting. Turfs not used within these periods shall be regarded as topsoil.

7.   As *required by the Contract*, newly turfed areas on slopes of cuttings and embankments shall be secured by netting.

218.   Filling Existing Watercourses
1.   Where watercourses have been diverted the original channels shall be cleared of all vegetation and soft deposits and filled in with selected fill deposited and compacted as specified in Clauses 211 and 212.

219.   Clearing Existing Ditches
1.   Where *required by the Contract* existing ditches shall be cleared by removing vegetation and deposits. The sides shall be trimmed, the bottoms uniformly graded and the ditches kept clean and maintained for the period of execution of the Works. Material removed from existing ditches shall be disposed of in tips provided by the Contractor off the site.

220.   Gabions
1.   Gabions shall be assembled in accordance with the manufacturers instructions. They shall be filled with selected uniformly graded granular material consisting of natural gravel, crushed

rock other than argillaceous rock, crushed concrete or any combination thereof. The grading of the fill material shall be such as to minimise the amount of voids in the gabions. The maximum size of the fill material shall not exceed two thirds of the minimum dimension of the gabion or 200 mm whichever is the smaller. The minimum size of the fill shall not be less than the size of the mesh opening.

2.   Filling of gabions shall be carried out by hand with an allowance for consolidation of fill so as to minimise distortion during construction. Gabion units shall, where appropriate be maintained square with vertical sides during filling. Internal tie wires shall be inserted and units tensioned in accordance with the manufacturers instructions.

3.   The gabion mesh shall be manufactured from wire complying with BS 1052 having a minimum core dia. of 2.2 mm or otherwise as *required by the Contract*. The wire shall be galvanised in compliance with BS 443 and where *required by the Contract*, be coated with a minimum thickness of 0.55mm of dark green or blue PVC which shall be capable of resisting the effects of immersion in sea water, exposure to ultra violet radiation and abrasion.

Materials

301. Compliance with British Standards

1. Where an appropriate British Standard or equivalent exists the materials and products incorporated in the works should comply with its relevant provisions. They should also be Kitemarked where appropriate, though the mark of conformity of any other third party certification body accredited by the National Accreditation Council for Certification Bodies or equivalent is an acceptable alternative.

302. Materials in Contact with Potable Water

1. All materials used in the construction of the temporary or permanent works which will be in contact with potable water shall be approved by the Water Research Centre and be listed in the "Water Fittings and Materials Directory" as published by the Water Research Centre.
In the case of non-metallic products, they shall comply with BS 6920.

303. Admixtures for Concrete

1. Admixtures shall comply with
       BS 1014 (Pigments)
       BS 3892 (Pulverized fuel ash)
       BS 5075:Part 1 (Accelerating, retarding and water reducing admixtures)
       BS 5075:Part 1 (Air Entraining Admixtures)
unless *required by the Contract* or approved.

304. Aggregates for Concrete

1. Aggregates shall consist of naturally occurring material complying with BS 882. If approved the coarse aggregates may consist of crushed air cooled blast furnace slag complying with BS 1047.

2. Flakiness index when determined by the sieve method described in BS 812 shall not exceed 35 for any size of coarse aggregate.

3. For structural concrete of specified compressive strength of 40 N/mm^2 or more at 28 days, the 'ten per cent fines' value of the coarse aggregate determined in accordance with BS 812 shall not be less than 100 kN and for other structural concrete not less than 50 kN.

4. The drying shrinkage value of the aggregate shall be as *required by the Contract*.

305. Bituminous Macadam Surfacing

1. Single Course Bitumen Macadam for Roadways. The material shall be made with 40 mm nominal size hard, clean, durable crushed rock, slag or gravel aggregate and shall comply with BS 4987. The aggregate shall have the polished stone value *required by the Contract*.

2. Two Course Bitumen Macadam for Roadways. The base course shall be made with 40 mm nominal size hard, clean, durable crushed rock, slag or gravel aggregate and shall comply with BS 4987.
The wearing course shall be made with 10 mm nominal size hard, clean, durable crushed rock, slag or gravel aggregate and shall comply with BS 4987, Tables 45-48. The aggregate shall have the polished stone value *required by the Contract*.

3. Coarse cold asphalt for wearing course of roadways shall comply with BS 4987, The aggregate shall have the polished stone value *required by the Contract*.

4. Hot processed rolled asphalt shall comply with BS 594. The penetration of the asphaltic cement, the polished stone value of the aggregate, and the coarse aggregate content shall be as *required by the Contract*.

5. Bituminous sealing grit shall comply with BS 4987 in respect of manufacture and application.

6.   Two Course Bitumen Macadam for Footpaths shall be as follows:-

   (a)   The base course shall be made with 20 mm nominal size hard, clean, durable crushed rock, slag or gravel aggregate and shall comply with BS 4987.

   (b)   The wearing course shall be made with 6 mm nominal size hard, clean, durable crushed rock, slag or gravel aggregate and shall comply with BS 4987.

   (c)   The chippings shall be uncoated 6.3 mm nominal size crushed rock of approved colour and shall comply with BS 63.

   (d)   The bitumen shall comply with BS 3690.

7.   Tack coat shall consist of an anionic bituminous emulsion to comply with BS 434, Type 1C having a viscosity less than 5° Engler and containing 35 per cent bitumen.

306.   Bolts, Nuts and Fastenings
1.   Bolts, nuts and washers shall comply with BS 916, BS 1769 and BS 3410 as *required by the Contract*.

2.   High strength friction grip bolts shall comply with BS 4395 and shall be fitted in accordance with BS 4604.

3.   Fastenings shall comply with BS 6104 and BS 6105.

307.   Bond Breaking Compound for Dowel Bars
1.   Bond breaking compound shall consist of 66 per cent of 200 pen bitumen blended hot with 14 per cent light creosote oil and, when cold, brought to the consistency of paint by the addition of 20 per cent solvent naptha or other approved compound meeting the following requirements:-

   (a)   It shall not affect the setting of concrete, and

   (b)   the average bond stress on bars coated with the compound with half their length cast into concrete specimens and subjected to pull out tests at 7 days shall not exceed 0.14N/mm^2 and the total movement of the dowel bar relative to the concrete shall not be less than 0.25 mm at that stress. The concrete specimens shall be 150 mm by 150 mm in section and 450 mm long and made with the same mix proportions as used in the Works.

308.   Bricks
1.   Bricks shall comply with BS 3921 or BS 6073 as *required by the Contract*.

2.   Bricks for the construction of manholes, inspection chambers, catchpits and the like shall be Class B clay engineering bricks complying with BS 3921.

3.   Samples of all bricks intended for use in the Permanent Works shall be submitted for approval.

309.   Cast Stone
1.   Cast stone shall comply with BS 1217. Samples of the finished stone shall be submitted for approval.

2.   All stones shall be protected from damage during transport.

310.   Cement
1.   Ordinary Portland cement and rapid hardening Portland cement shall comply with BS 12.

2.   Portland blast furnace cement shall comply with BS 146.

3.   Sulphate resisting Portland cement shall comply with BS 4027.

4.   High alumina cement shall comply with BS 915.

5.   Low heat cement shall comply with either BS 1370 or BS 4246.

6.   Supersulphated cement shall comply with BS 4248.

7.   White or coloured Portland cement shall comply with the physical requirements of BS 12 and pigments shall be inorganic oxide pigments, either natural or synthetic in origin, complying with the requirements of BS 1014. Pigments whether added just before mixing or by the cement manufacturer shall be incorporated in the proportions approved.

311. Cement Grout
1.   Cement grout shall be mixed in the proportions indicated in Table 300A using the minimum quantity of water to ensure the necessary fluidity and to render it capable of penetrating the work.

TABLE 300A

Class	Nominal mix by weight		
	Cement	Sand	PFC
G1	1	-	-
G2	1	3	-
G3	1	10	-
G4	1	-	10
G5	1	-	4
G6	1	-	½

2.   Cement grout shall be used within one hour of mixing, unless it contains a retardant admixture.

3.   Sulphate resisting cement shall not be used as a constituent of grouts containing pulverised fuel ash.

312. Clay Puddle
1.   Clay puddle shall be impervious to water and free from stones, roots or any matter likely to detract from this function. It shall be of a consistency suitable for punning in the required position in the Works.

313. Concrete Pipes for Pipejacking
1.   All concrete pipes for use in pipe jacking shall comply with BS 5911 and be of at least strength class "H". They shall not be supplied to site at less than 28 days old.

2.   Thrusting surfaces shall be square to the pipe axis and free from significant undulations and protuberances.

314. Creosote
1.   Creosote shall comply with BS 144.

26

315. Curing Compounds

1.   Aluminised curing compound when applied as specified by Clause 429 by a mechanical sprayer shall become stable and impervious to evaporation of water from the concrete surface within 60 minutes after application. The curing compound shall contain sufficient flake aluminium in finely divided dispersion to produce a complete coverage of the sprayed surface with a metallic finish. The curing compound shall not react chemically with the concrete to be cured and shall not crack, peel or disintegrate within three weeks after application.

2.   Resinous curing compound shall be an approved, proprietary, tinted liquid composition.

316. Damp Proof Course

1.   Damp proof course shall be bitumen hessian based damp proof course weighing not less than 4.36 kg/m^2 or other approved material complying with BS 743.

317. Doors, Frames and Linings

1.   Doors shall comply with BS 459.

2.   Wood door frames and linings shall comply with BS 1567 or BS 459.

318. Dowel Bars and Tie Bars for Concrete Roads

1.   Dowel bars shall be mild steel. Tie bars shall be mild steel bars or deformed bars of high yield steel. All bars shall comply with BS 4449.

2.   Dowel bars shall be 20 mm dia. by 500 mm long, straight, free from burred edges, or other irregularities and shall have their sliding ends sawn or, if approved, sheared.

3.   Tie bars shall be 12 mm dia. by 1 m long.

319. Fencing

1.   Fencing shall comply with the relevant section of BS 1722.

320. Fencing Wire

1.   Fencing wire shall be of mild steel and comply with BS 4102.

321. Filter Media

1.   General
   (a)   Filter media for biological filters and sludge drying beds shall be crushed stone or other durable, hard material of suitable shape and roughness approved in writing and complying with BS 1438.

2.   Biological Filters
   (a)   The top layer shall comply with the grading limits in BS 1438:Table 1 for 50 mm nominal maximum size.

   (b)   The bottom layer shall pass a 150 mm ring and be retained on a 75 mm ring.

3.   Sludge Drying Beds
   (a)   Filter media for sludge drying beds without full tile coverage shall be graded as follows:-

      (i)   Passing a 150 mm ring and retained on a 100 mm ring.

      (ii)   Passing a 50 mm ring and retained on a 25 mm ring.

      (iii)   Passing a 25 mm ring and retained on a 19 mm ring.

(b)   Filter media for sludge drying beds with full tile coverage shall comply with the grading limits of BS 1438 for 10 mm nominal maximum size except that all the media is to be retained on a 4.75 mm sieve.

(c)   Sand for sludge drying beds shall comply with the grading limits in BS 882: Table 2 for Grading Zone 1 and shall approach as nearly as possible the coarser limit of the Zone.

(d)   Ash for sludge drying beds shall be screened, dry, hard, well burnt and free from clinker, blaes, dust or any other deleterious matter. It shall have a grading generally equivalent to the grading limits of BS 882 Table 5 Grading Zone C and shall approach as nearly as possible the coarse limit of this zone.

322. Filter Tiles
1.   Filter and sludge drying bed tiles shall be first quality, made from good fireclay and must be hard, homogeneous and impervious, and free from cracks or imperfections. They shall be from an approved manufacturer and shall be straight, true and of uniform thickness throughout.

323. Floor Tiles
1.   Clay tiles for flooring shall be of first quality and shall comply with BS 1286.

324. Formwork Release Agents
1.   Formwork Release Agents shall be one of the following:-

(a)   Neat oils with surfactants for use on steel, timber and plywood faces.

(b)   Mould cream emulsions for use on timber and plywoods.

(c)   Chemical release agents for use on all types of form face for high quality finish.

325. Gates and Posts
1.   Domestic and field gates shall comply with BS 4092 and BS 3470 respectively. Posts shall comply with BS 3470.

326. Glazing
1.   Glass shall comply with BS 952.

2.   Putty for glazing in timber sashes shall comply with BS 544.

3.   Putty for glazing in aluminium sashes shall be a non setting compound and shall comply with BS 6262.

4.   Bedding compounds for double glazing units shall be as *required by the Contract*.

327. Gullies, Gully Gratings and Frames
1.   Precast concrete gullies shall be unreinforced and shall comply with BS 556.

2.   Glazed ware gullies shall comply with BS 539 in respect of round street gullies.

3.   Cast iron gullies shall be of approved manufacture and as *required by the Contract*.

4.   Cast iron and cast steel gully gratings, covers and frames shall comply with BS 497.

5.   Gullies made of polypropylene, polyethylene, uPVC or other approved plastic materials shall comply with BS 5911.

328. Handrails
1. Handrails in manholes shall be formed from 25 mm dia. solid mild steel bar galvanised after manufacture.

2. Handrails for other purposes shall be as *required by the Contract*.

329. Hardcore
1. Hardcore for other than roadworks shall be hard durable inert material free from dust, wood, rubbish and organic material. It shall be graded from 225 mm to 75mm.

330. Hydrated Lime
1. Hydrated lime shall comply with BS 890.

331. Joinery Timber
1. Joinery timber shall comply with BS 1186.

332. Joint Sealing Compound and Sealant
1. Poured joint sealing compound shall consist of hot poured rubber bitumen compound complying with BS 2499 or cold poured complying with BS 5212 as *required by the Contract*.

2. Cold applied joint sealing compound for jointing precast concrete manhole units shall be filled bituminous putty of approved quality suitable for application by trowel or gun. The compound shall have good adhesion and elastic properties. If approved, preformed jointing strip material may be used.

3. Two part polysulphide based sealants shall comply with BS 4254.

4. Polyurethane based sealants shall be as *required by the Contract*.

333. Joints with Bitumen Coating
1. If *required by the Contract*, bitumen coating of joints shall be of approved material, applied not less than 2 mm thick. The bitumen shall be applied sufficiently in advance of concreting to ensure that it is properly hardened before concrete is placed against it.

334. Manhole Covers and Frames
1. Manhole covers and frames shall be of grey or ductile iron and shall comply with BS 497.

335. Manhole Ladders
1. Manhole ladders and fixings shall be of mild steel complying with BS 449 galvanised after manufacture in accordance with BS 729 with a surface coating of at least 600 g/m² of surface area or a thickness of 85 microns.

2. The stringers shall be 64 mm by 19 mm section and the rungs 25 mm dia.
The stringers shall be placed not less than 380 mm apart with approved fixing brackets of material equal to the stringers located at centres not exceeding 2m with a minimum of two pairs per ladder. The brackets shall be of sufficient length to give a clearance of 230 mm behind the rungs. The rungs shall be at 230 mm centres and fixed to the stringers in accordance with BS 4211.

336. Manhole Safety Chains
1. Manhole safety chain shall be galvanised mild steel short link chain and shall comply with BS 6405 Class 1.

2. The chain length shall be as *required by the Contract* with one end securely attached to 16 mm dia. galvanised mild steel eyebolt and the other end securely attached to a suitable galvanised wrought iron hook.

337. Manhole Step Irons
1. Manhole step irons shall comply with BS 1247.

2. For brick manholes, step irons shall be galvanised malleable cast iron general purpose pattern and shall have 230 mm long tails.

3. For precast concrete manholes, step irons shall be galvanised malleable cast iron precast concrete manhole pattern with 80 mm long tails.

338. Metal Flooring
1. Mild steel and aluminium alloy industrial open metal flooring shall comply with BS 4592.

2. Steel floor plate shall be Admiralty pattern or Supergrip pattern chequer plate as *required by the Contract* with holes drilled for lifting keys and shall be hot dip galvanised in accordance with BS 729.

339. Mortar
1. Mortar shall be mixed only as and when required in the relevant proportions indicated in Table 300B, until its colour and consistency are uniform. The constituent materials shall be accurately gauged, allowance being made for bulking of sand.

2. Ready mixed lime and sand for mortar and ready to use retarded mortar shall comply with BS 4721.

3. Mortar which has begun to set or which has been site mixed for a period of more than one hour in the case of Classes M1, M2, M5 and M6, and two hours in the case of Classes M3, M4, M7 and M8, shall not be used. Mortar plasticisers shall comply with BS 4887 and shall be used in accordance with the manufacturers' instructions.

TABLE 300B

Class	Cement: lime : sand	Cement: sand with plasticiser	Class	cement: sand
M1	1: 0 to ¼: 3	1: 2½ to 3	M5	1: 2 to 2½
M2	1: ½: 4 to 4½	1: 3 to 4	M6	1: 2½ to 3½
M3	1: 1: 5 to 6	1: 5 to 6	M7	1: 4 to 5
M4	1: 2: 8 to 9	1: 7 to 8	M8	1: 5 to 6½

Nominal mix by volume

340. Nails
1. Nails shall comply with BS 1202.

341. Paint and other Protective Coatings for Steelwork and Woodwork

1. General

   (a) Paint shall comply with BS 5493. Paints forming part of any one painting system shall be obtained from the same approved source.

2. Colours

   (a) Colours shall comply with BS 4800.

3. Metal Coatings

   (a) Galvanised coatings shall comply with BS 729 and shall have a surface coating of not less than 600 g/m^2 zinc applied by the hot dip process.

   (b) Sherardized coatings shall comply with BS 729.

   (c) Sprayed metal coatings shall comply with BS 2569.

4. Priming Paints

   (a) Lead based priming paints shall comply with BS 2523.

   (b) Calcium plumbate priming paints shall comply with BS 3698.

   (c) Non toxic and low lead priming paints shall comply with BS 5082 and BS 2358.

5. Constituents of Paints

   (a) Chilled iron shot and grit shall comply with BS 2451.

   (b) Natural red oxides of iron for paints shall comply with BS 3981.

   (c) Manufactured red oxides of iron for paints, excluding venetian red, shall comply with BS 3981.

   (d) Lead and zinc chromes for paints shall comply with BS 282 and BS 389.

   (e) Aluminium flake pigments (powder and paste) for paints shall comply with BS 388.

   (f) Calcium plumbate for paints shall comply with BS 3699.

6. Paint Removers

   (a) Water rinsable and solvent rinsable paint removers shall comply with BS 3761.

7. Black Bituminous Coating Solution for Steelwork

   (a) Black bituminous coating solution for cold application shall comply with BS 3416, Type 1.

342. Pipe Bedding Material

1. Granular bedding Type A for pipes shall consist of aggregates from natural sources complying with BS 882. Grading shall comply with BS 882 Table 4 as follows:-

   Material X1 :
   20 mm nominal size graded aggregate, for use with pipes up to 525 mm nominal diameter.

   > 90 - 100% passing 20 mm sieve
   > 30 - 60% passing 10 mm sieve
   > 0 - 10% passing 5 mm sieve

   Material X2 :
   40 mm nominal size graded aggregate, for use with pipes over 525 mm diameter.

   > 90 - 100% passing 37.5 mm sieve
   > 35 - 70% passing 20 mm sieve
   > 10 - 40% passing 10 mm sieve
   > 0 - 5% passing 5 mm sieve

Material Y1 :
20 mm nominal size, single size aggregate, for use with pipes up to 525 mm nominal diameter.

     85 - 100% passing 20 mm sieve
       0 - 25% passing 10 mm sieve
       0 - 5% passing 5 mm sieve

Material Y2 :
40 mm nominal size, single size aggregate, for use with pipes up to 525 mm nominal diameter.

     85 - 100% passing 37.5 mm sieve
       0 - 25% passing 20 mm sieve
       0 - 5% passing 5 mm sieve

Note: a. Gravel is not acceptable for Material X2 and Y2.
       b. The material to be used for bedding and surround for concrete pipes shall not contain more than 0.3 per cent sulphate expressed as sulphur trioxide.

2.   Selected fill Type B shall be uniform readily compactable material free from vegetable matter, building rubbish, frozen soil, material susceptible to spontaneous combustion and clay lumps and stones retained on 75 mm sieve and 37.5 mm sieve respectively.

3.   Granular bedding Type C shall be as for Type A but to pass a 10 mm sieve.

4.   Sand for bedding pipes shall comply with the provisions of BS 882, Table 5, Grading Zone C.

5.   Type E material for backfilling field or French drains shall be hard clean crushed rock or gravel having a grading within the following limits:-

          100% passing 63 mm sieve
     85 - 100% passing 37.5 mm sieve
      0 - 20% passing 20 mm sieve
      0 - 5% passing 10 mm sieve

343. Pipes, Fittings and Joints

1.   Ductile iron pipes and fittings shall comply with BS 4772. They shall be coated with bitumen internally and externally, except parts to be encased in concrete. DI pipes and fittings for water mains shall first be cement mortar lined internally before coating with bitumen.

2.   Vitrified clay pipes and pipeline fittings shall comply with BS 65 and be supplied complete with the manufacturer's flexible integral or sleeve joint.

3.   Perforated clay pipes and fittings for use in the constuction of French drains shall comply with BS 65.

4.   Clayware field drain pipes shall comply with BS 1196.

5.   Unreinforced and reinforced concrete pipes and fittings shall comply with BS 5911 and be supplied with approved flexible joints.

6.   Concrete pipes and fittings strengthened by alkali-resistant glass fibre rovings shall comply with BS 5911.

7.   Prestressed concrete pipes including fittings shall comply with BS 4625. Pipes and fittings for drainage, sewers and drains shall comply with BS 5178. Pipes and fittings shall be steam cured.

8.   Concrete porous pipes shall comply with BS 1194.

9.   uPVC pressure pipes, joints and fittings shall comply with BS 3505.

10.   uPVC pipes, joints and fittings for gravity sewers and drains shall comply with BS 4660 or BS 5481.

11.   uPVC solid wall concentric external rib reinforced sewer pipe shall comply with the relevant provisions of Information and Guidance Note 4-31-05 published by the WAA Sewers and Water Mains Committee.

12.   Asbestos cement pressure pipes, joints and fittings shall comply with BS 486.

13.   Asbestos cement pipes, joints and fittings for sewers shall comply with BS 3656.

14.   Glass fibre reinforced plastic pipes and fittings shall comply with BS 5480.

15.   Acrylonitrile butadiene styrene pressure pipes and fittings shall comply with BS 5391.

16.   Polyethylene pipes for cold water services shall comply with BS 6572, for below ground, and BS 6730 for above ground.

17.   Flanges for pipes and fittings shall comply with BS 4505 for 16 bar nominal pressure rating.

18.   Gaskets for flanged pipe joints shall be of the inside bolt circle type. The dimensions of gaskets shall comply with BS 4865. Gaskets for watermains and sewerage shall be manufactured from material complying with BS 2494 for Type 1 and Type 2 respectively.

19.   Rubber joint rings for water mains and sewers shall be Types 1 and 2 respectively complying with BS 2494 and shall be obtained from the pipe manufacturer.

20.   Joint lubricants shall have no deleterious effects on either the joint rings or pipes. Only approved lubricants shall be used for jointing water mains.

21.   Bolts, nuts and washers for flanged joints shall be cadmium plated and shall comply with BS 4504. Bolts shall have a minimum ultimate strength of 433 N/mm^2.

22.   Steel pipe ends, flanged specials and fittings shall be supplied complete with protective bolsters, caps or discs.

344.   Plaster
1.   Plaster shall be premixed lightweight aggregate gypsum plaster and shall comply with BS 1191.

345.   Plasterboard
1.   Plasterboard shall be gypsum wallboard and shall comply with BS 1230.

346.   Plumbing Materials
1.   Rainwater Conductors and Fittings

   (a)   Cast iron rainwater conductors shall be medium grade, coated inside and outside and shall comply with BS 460.

(b)   Aluminium rainwater conductors shall comply with BS 2997.

(c)   uPVC rainwater goods shall comply with BS 4576.

2. Soil and Waste Pipes and Fittings
    (a)   Cast iron soil and waste pipes shall be medium grade, coated with approved protective solution inside and outside and shall comply with BS 416.

    (b)   uPVC soil and waste pipes and fittings shall comply with BS 4514.

3. Water Pipes and Fittings
    (a)   Copper piping for underground use shall be fully annealed or semi-hard drawn as *required by the Contract* and shall comply with BS 2871. Copper piping for general use above ground shall comply with BS 2871.

    (b)   Copper pipe fittings shall comply with BS 864. Capillary fittings shall be of the integral solder ring pattern. Type A or B compression fittings shall be used with semi-hard pipes. Types A or B compression fittings for use on underground pipework shall be of gunmetal alloy.

    (c)   Underground stop-cocks shall be of the Scottish plug cock pattern or screwdown pattern and shall comply with BS 2580.

    (d)   Taps and stop valves shall be of the screwdown pattern and shall comply with BS 1010, fitted with washers complying with BS 3457. Hose taps and hose connections shall have outlet noses screwed to comply with BS 1010, Table 14.

    (e)   Chromium plating to exposed copper piping and fittings shall be as *required by the Contract* and shall comply with BS 1224, Classification No. 3C.

    (f)   Polythene tubing shall comply with BS 1972 for heavy gauge or BS 3284 Class C for high density tubing. Pipe fittings for use with polythene tubing shall be approved compression fittings of copper alloy, gunmetal or plastic.

    (g)   Propylene copolymer pipes shall comply with BS 4991 and shall be of the Class *required by the Contract*.

    (h)   Pipe supports shall be approved polypropylene clips.

4. Cisterns
    (a)   Polythene or polypropylene cisterns shall comply with BS 4213. Galvanised cisterns shall comply with BS 417, Grade A. They shall be complete with covers and shall be fitted with a warning pipe, ball tap or float-operated valve complying with BS 1212 and have an opening in the bottom for cleansing. Floats shall comply with BS 1968 Class C or BS 2456.

5. Connections
    (a)   Connections to asbestos cement or plastic pipes shall be made with gunmetal saddles, bolts and rubber washers or combined ferrule strap as supplied by the pipe manufacturer.

347. Precast Concrete
1. Precast concrete blocks shall comply with BS 6073.

2. Precast concrete copes shall comply with BS 5642:Part 2.

3. Precast concrete slabs shall be hydraulically pressed and shall comply with BS 368. The slabs shall be 50 mm thick and, except where cutting is necessary, of a uniform width of 600 mm and minimum length of 450 mm and a maximum length of 900mm.

4. Precast concrete lintels shall comply with BS 5977:Parts 1 and 2.

5. Precast concrete kerbs, channels and edgings shall be hydraulically pressed and they and precast concrete quadrants shall comply with BS 340.

6. Precast concrete sills shall comply with BS 5642.

7. Precast, prestressed concrete units shall comply with BS 8110.

348. Precast Concrete Manholes and Valve Chambers
1. Precast concrete manhole sections shall be reinforced and shall comply with BS 5911.

2. Precast concrete valve chambers shall be of interlocking sections, capable of adjustment for height, reinforced and shall comply with BS 5911.

3. The relevant absorption tests required by BS 5911 shall be carried out on one in every fifty sections.

349. Preformed Joint Filler for Concrete Roads
1. Preformed joint filler shall be not greater than 25 mm thick nor less than 12 mm thick as *required by the Contract* within a tolerance of ± 1.5 mm. It shall be 25 mm less in depth than the thickness of the slab within a tolerance of ± 3 mm and in suitable lengths each not less than 1.2 m. Holes to accommodate dowel bars shall be accurately bored or punched out to be a sliding fit on the dowel bars.

2. The joint filler material shall be of approved quality such that it can be satisfactorily installed in position at the joint and shall be waterproof, compressible and non-extruding, with a high recovery factor after compression at temperatures below 49°C.

350. Protective Paste, Mastic and Tape for Ferrous Joints
1. The paste shall be a stable neutral compound based on saturated petroleum hydrocarbons, containing corrosion inhibitors and inert siliceous fillers and shall be adhesive and non hardening.

2. Mastic shall be the paste as in Clause 350.1 but in addition shall contain vegetable and mineral bonding fibres and shall be self supporting when applied.

3. Tape shall be an open weave, inert, highly absorbent cloth, impregnated and coated liberally on both sides with the paste.

4. These materials shall be made by an approved manufacturer.

351. PTFE Tape
1. PFTE tape for thread sealing applications shall comply with BS 4375.

352. Ready Mixed Concrete
1. Ready mixed concrete shall be as *required by the Contract* and shall comply with BS 5328.

353. Roof Cladding
1. Sheet type roof cladding shall comply with BS 2989.

354. Roofing Felts
1. Roofing felts shall comply with BS 747:Part 2.

355. Roofing Slates and Tiles

1. Roofing slates shall comply with BS 680.

2. Clay roofing tiles shall comply with BS 402.

3. Concrete tiles shall comply with BS 413.

4. Ridge and hip tiles shall comply with BS 402 or BS 473 for butt jointed ridge tiles as appropriate and shall blend with the colour of the slating.

5. Asbestos cement slates, corrugated sheets and semi-compressed flat sheets shall comply with BS 690.

356. Sand

1. Plaster sand shall comply with BS 1199 and BS 1200. If directed the sand shall be passed through a 3 mm square mesh sieve.

357. Setts

1. Granite or whinstone setts shall be squared, hammer dressed, and shall comply with BS 435.

358. Softwood Flooring

1. Softwood flooring shall be 25 mm tongued and grooved boarding or as *required by the Contract* and shall comply with BS 1297.

2. Resin bonded wood chipboard flooring shall comply with BS 5669.

359. Steel Arch Rib Support

1. Steel arch rib supports shall be cold rolled or fabricated from sections of mild steel to BS 4360 Grade 43A.

360. Steel Reinforcement

1. Mild steel bar reinforcement shall comply with BS 4449.

2. Deformed high yield steel bar reinforcement shall comply with BS 4449.

3. Steel fabric reinforcement shall comply with BS 4483. The wires shall be welded at the intersections and the fabric shall be delivered to the site in flat mats.

4. The Contractor shall provide the Engineer with certificates from the manufacturers that all steel supplied is in accordance with these conditions.

5. Tying wire shall be either:-
    (a)   1.625 mm dia. soft annealed iron wire, or

    (b)   1.218 mm dia. stainless steel wire.

361. Steel Tubes and Sections

1. Steel tubes and sections for fence gates shall comply with BS 6323 and BS 4630 respectively. Welding shall comply with BS 5135.

362. Structural Steel and Aluminium

1. Weldable structural steels shall comply with BS 4360.

2.   Structural steel sections shall comply with BS 4 or BS 4848 as appropriate.

3.   Cold rolled steel sections shall comply with BS 2994.

4.   Steel tubes for general purposes shall comply with BS 6323.

5.   Steel castings and forgings shall comply with BS 3100 or BS 29 as *required by the Contract*.

6.   Aluminium plate, sheet and strip shall comply with BS 1470.

7.   Sections for structural purposes shall comply with BS 1161.

363. Sub-base and Roadbase

1.   Sub-base and roadbase materials shall be granular, frost resistant and comprise crushed rock, crushed slag, crushed concrete or well burnt non-plastic shale. The material shall be well graded and lie within the following limits:-

TABLE 300C

BS Sieve Size	Range of Grading: Percentage by Weight Passing
75 mm	100
37.5 mm	85-100
10 mm	40-70
5 mm	25-45
600 microns	8-22
75 microns	0-10

The particle size shall be determined in accordance with BS 1377.

2.   The material passing 425 N/m sieve, when tested in accordance with BS 1377, shall be non-plastic.

364. Surface Boxes

1.   Surface boxes shall comply with BS 5834.

365. Terrazzo Dividing Strips

1.   Terrazzo dividing strips shall be of brass, copper, zinc, ebonite or plastic as *required by the Contract*. The depth of the strips shall be not less than the depth of the screed coat plus terrazzo paving with a minimum strip width of 3mm.

366. Top Soil for Soiling Embankments etc.

1.   Top soil shall comply with BS 3882.

367. Turf
1. Turf shall comply with BS 3969.

368. Valves and Other Fittings
1. All valves, penstocks, headstocks, brackets and other fittings shall be to the patterns *required by the Contract* and shall be from an approved manufacturer.

2. Fire hydrants shall comply with BS 750 and shall be fitted with a self-operating frost valve or drilled plug on the drain boss outlet.

369. Wall Ties
1. Wall ties shall comply with BS 1243.

370. Wall Tiles
1. Wall tiles shall be 150 mm square by 10 mm thick glazed tiles with cope and cove tiles and shall comply with BS 6431.

371. Water for Use with Cement
1. If water for the Works is not available from the public supply, approval shall be obtained regarding the source of supply and manner of its use. When directed the Contractor shall arrange for tests of the water to be carried out in accordance with BS 3148. Water from the sea or tidal rivers shall not be used for structural concrete.

372. Waterproof Underlay
1. Waterproof underlay shall consist of either waterproof paper complying with BS 152 :Grade BIF or approved 250 grade or 500 grade impermeable plastic sheeting as *required by the Contract*.

373. Windows
1. Wood windows shall be as *required by the Contract* and shall be obtained from an approved supplier.

2. UPVC windows shall be as *required by the Contract* and shall be obtained from an approved supplier.

3. Aluminium alloy windows shall comply with BS 4873.

4. Steel windows shall comply with BS 6510.

Formwork and Concrete

401. General
1.   Formwork and concrete shall comply with:
   (a)   BS 8007 for aqueous liquid retaining concrete structures,

   (b)   BS 8110: Part 1 for all reinforced and unreinforced concrete structures,

   (c)   BS 5328 for concrete production, delivery, testing and compliance.

402.   Definition of Formwork
1.   Formwork shall include all temporary or permanent forms required for forming the concrete, together with all temporary construction required for their support.

403.   Adequacy of Formwork
1.   The Contractor shall be responsible for the design and construction of all temporary formwork. Formwork shall comply with BS 8110.

2.   The design and construction of formwork shall take account of safety and of the surface finish required.

3.   Formwork and its supports shall maintain their correct position and be to correct shape and profile so that the final concrete structure is within the dimensional tolerances specified in Table 400A. The formwork shall be sufficiently rigid and tight to prevent loss of cement grout or fines from the fresh concrete.

404.   Ties and Formwork Supports in Concrete
1.   The material, type and position of any tie or fixing in concrete shall be approved. The whole or part of each tie or fixing shall be capable of being removed so that any part remaining embedded in the concrete shall be no nearer to the surface of the concrete than the specified thickness of cover to the reinforcement in the same member. Formwork spacers left in situ shall be of such materials and designs as will be durable, avoid corrosion of the reinforcement and spalling of the concrete cover and shall prevent the passage of moisture. In mass concrete, the minimum cover to embedded parts shall be 40 mm.

2.   In structural concrete, holes left after the removal of ties or fixings shall be carefully cleaned out and filled with mortar which shall include an approved non-shrinking agent.
The mortar filling of the holes in water retaining concrete shall be stopped off 12 mm from the surface and the remainder of the recess primed and pointed with an approved sealing compound or as *required by the Contract.*

405.   Top Formwork
1.   Top formwork shall be used on any concrete face steeper than 15° to the horizontal.

406.   Arrises
1.   All exposed arrises shall have 25 mm chamfers.

407.   Removal of Debris
1.   All rubbish, debris and water shall be removed from the interior of forms before concrete is placed and temporary openings shall be provided in the formwork to facilitate their removal. The faces of the forms in contact with the concrete shall be clean.

408.   Permanent Forms and Formwork
1.   Permanent formwork shall be of approved materials as *required by the Contract* and shall be fixed to the structure by approved means. The formwork shall be sufficiently rigid and tight to prevent loss of cement grout or fines from the fresh concrete.

TABLE 400A Tolerances for Concrete Surfaces

Category	Irregularity	Tolerances (millimetres)					
		Formed Surfaces			Unformed Surfaces		
		A	B and D	C and E	U/A	U/B	U/C
General Structural	Departure from alignment and grade	+ 5 − 10	± 5	±5	± 10	± 5	± 3
	Variations in cross-section dimension	+ 10 − 5	+ 10 − 5	± 5	N/A	N/A	N/A
	Abrupt	5	0	0	5	0	0
	Deviation from template	± 10	± 5	± 5	± 10	± 5	± 3
Areas where Plant is to be installed	Departure from alignment and grade	N/A	N/A	± 3	N/A	N/A	N/A
	Variations in cross-section dimensions	N/A	N/A	± 3	N/A	N/A	N/A
	Abrupt	N/A	N/A	0	N/A	N/A	0
	Deviation from template	N/A	N/A	± 3	N/A	N/A	± 3
Measuring Flume Contours	Departure from alignment and grade	N/A	N/A	± 2	N/A	N/A	± 2
	Abrupt	N/A	N/A	0	N/A	N/A	0
	Deviation from template	N/A	N/A	± 2	N/A	N/A	± 2

N/A denotes not applicable

NOTE 1: The template to be used in determining the deviation in long dimensions shall be:-
(a) For straight surfaces 2 metres
(b) For curved surfaces 1 metre

NOTE 2: For illustrations of the types of irregularity see 'A Guide to Specifying Concrete' Part 1 published by the Institution of Civil Engineers.

409. Preparation of Formwork before Concreting

1. The faces of the forms in contact with the concrete shall, except for permanent formwork, be coated with an approved release agent to prevent adhesion to the concrete. The release agent shall be applied strictly in accordance with the manufacturer's instructions so as to provide a thin uniform coating and shall not come into contact with the reinforcement or prestressing tendons and anchorages. Only one type of release agent shall be used in formwork to concrete which will be visible in the finished Permanent Works.

410. Notice of Intention to Place Concrete

1. The Contractor shall give at least 24 hours notice, inclusive of one full working day, of his intention to place concrete to allow the Engineer reasonable time to check the formwork and reinforcement. No checking shall commence until all preparatory work has been completed. Final written approval of the preparation of the formwork shall be obtained immediately before concreting begins.

411. Types of Finish, Formed Surfaces

1. The types of finish on formed surfaces shall be in accordance with BS 8110 and are as follows:-

   (a)   Type A finish. This finish shall be obtained by the use of properly designed formwork or moulds of timber, plywood, plastics, concrete or steel. Small blemishes caused by entrapped air or water may be expected, but the surface shall be free from voids, honeycombing or other blemishes.

   (b)   Type B finish. This finish shall be obtained by the use of high quality concrete and formwork. The concrete shall be thoroughly compacted and all surfaces shall be true, with clean arrises. Only very minor surface blemishes shall occur, with no staining or discoloration from the release agent.

   (c)   Type C finish. This finish shall be obtained by first producing a Type B finish. The surface shall then be improved by carefully removing all fins and other projections, thoroughly washing down, and then filling the most noticeable surface blemishes with a cement and fine aggregate paste to match the colour of the original concrete. The release agent shall be carefully chosen to ensure that the concrete surface will not be stained or discoloured. After the concrete has been properly cured the face shall be rubbed down where necessary to produce a smooth and even surface.

Where a Type B or C finish is required, and patent formwork based on small pans is being used, it shall be faced with full sheets of plywood at least 9.5 mm thick and sanded flush at joints.

412. Type of Finish, Unformed Surfaces

1. The types of finish on unformed surfaces shall be as follows:

   (a)   Type U/A finish. This finish shall be obtained by tamping across the full width of the surface to produce a dense uniform texture true to level and grade. Surplus concrete shall be struck off by a straight edge immediately after compaction, leaving the surface plain with uniform ridges not exceeding 5 mm in height.

   (b)   Type U/B finish. This finish shall be obtained by first producing a Type U/A finish and then working the surface with a wooden float to produce a uniform finish free from screed or float marks. Floating shall be done only after excess surface water has had time to dissipate and the concrete has hardened sufficiently.

   (c)   Type U/C finish. This finish shall be obtained by first producing a Type U/B finish and then working the surface with a steel float to produce a smooth uniform finish free from float marks. Floating shall be carried out only after excess surface water has had time to dissipate and the concrete has hardened sufficiently.

413. Tolerances

1. The permissible tolerances in formed and unformed surfaces for the various classes of finish specified in Clauses 411 and 412 shall not exceed the limits shown in Table 400A.

414. Patent Formwork
1.   Patent formwork shall be used strictly in accordance with the manufacturer's instructions.

415. Storing and Cleaning of Steel Reinforcement
1.   Steel reinforcement shall be stored in clean conditions. Different types of reinforcement shall be stacked separately and suitably labelled for positive identification.

2.   Reinforcement shall not be subjected to mechanical damage or shock loading prior to embedment.

3.   Prior to concreting reinforcement shall be free from loose rust, loose mill scale, and other substances which will adversely affect the steel or concrete or reduce the bond.

416. Cutting and Bending Reinforcement
1.   Cutting and bending of reinforcement shall comply with BS 4466 and with BS 8110. Cutting and bending shall be done in a manner that will not injure the material.

2.   Reinforcement shall not be straightened or rebent.

417. Fixing Reinforcement
1.   Reinforcement shall be fixed and secured against displacement, in the positions *required by the Contract*, and the cover shall be within ± 5 mm of the specified cover. Ends of tying wire shall be turned into the main body of the concrete.

2.   Laps and joints shall be made in reinforcement only when *required by the Contract*.

3.   Reinforcement shall be welded only where *required by the Contract*. Welding procedures shall be subject to prior approval in writing.

4.   Reinforcement shall be supported in the correct position by approved methods. Spacers shall be of such materials and designs as will be durable, avoid corrosion of the reinforcement and spalling of the concrete cover and prevent the passage of moisture.

5.   The mix used for spacer blocks made from cement, sand and small aggregate shall be comparable in strength, durability, porosity and appearance to the surrounding concrete. Concrete spacer blocks made on the construction site shall not be used.

418. Concrete Mixes, General
1.   The workability of the concrete shall be decided by the Contractor, subject to the limitations *required by the Contract*.

2.   The workability of the concrete shall be measured by means of the slump test or other approved methods. The permissible workability shall be in accordance with Table 400B for Prescribed Mixes or, where *required by the Contract*, Table 400E for Designed Mixes.

419. Prescribed Mixes
1.   A prescribed mix is one for which the Contractor is responsible for supplying a concrete containing materials in the proportions *required by the Contract*.

2.   The grade of prescribed mix concrete is designated by a number, which will normally be the 28 day characteristic compressive strength in N/mm^2, prefixed by the letter 'C' and followed by the letter 'P'.

TABLE 400B Prescribed Mixes

1. Mass of dry aggregate to be used with 100 kg of cement

Grade of concrete	Nominal maximum size of aggregate *mm*	40		20		14		10	
	Workability	Medium	High	Medium	High	Medium	High	Medium	High
	Range of slump for standard sample *mm*	50-100	80-170	25-75	65-135	5-55	50-100	0-45	15-65
	Range for sample taken in accordance with BS 5328 *Clause 9.2 mm*	40-110	70-180	15-85	55-145	0-65	40-110	0.55	5-75
		kg	kg	kg	kg	kg	kg	kg	kg
C7.5P		1080	920	900	780	N/A	N/A	N/A	N/A
C10P		900	800	770	690	N/A	N/A	N/A	N/A
C15P	Total	790	690	680	580	N/A	N/A	N/A	N/A
C20P	Aggregate	660	600	600	530	560	470	510	420
C25P		560	510	510	460	490	410	450	370
C30P		510	460	460	400	410	360	380	320

N/A denotes not applicable

2. Percentage by mass of fine aggregate to total aggregate

Grade of concrete	Nominal maximum size of aggregate *mm*	40		20		14		10	
	Workability	Medium	High	Medium	High	Medium	High	Medium	High
C7.5P C10P C15P		30-45		35-50		N/A		N/A	
C20P	Grading C	35	40	40	45	45	50	50	55
C25P	M	30	30-35	30-35	35-40	35-40	40-45	40-45	5-50
C30P	F	25	25	25	30	30	35	35	40

N/A denotes not applicable

Notes on the use of tables 1 and 2

NOTE 1: The proportions given in the tables will normally provide concrete of the strength in N/mm^2 indicated by the grade except where poor control is associated with the use of poor materials.

NOTE 2: For grades C7.5P, C10P and C15P a range of fine-aggregate percentages is given, the lower percentage is applicable for finer materials such as grading F sand and the higher percentage to coarser materials such as grading C sand.

NOTE 3: For all grades, small adjustments in the percentage of fine aggregate may be required depending on the properties of the particular aggregates being used.

NOTE 4: For Grades C20P, C25P and C30P, and where high workability is required, it is advisable to check that the percentage of fine aggregate stated will product satisfactory concrete if the grading of the fine aggregates approaches the coarser limits of grading C or the finer limits of grading F.

44

3.   Prescribed mixes to be used for the permanent works shall be in accordance with Table 400B.

4.   Strength tests shall be carried out during the progress of the work as *required by the Contract.*

420.   Designed Mixes
1.   A designed mix is one for which the Contractor is responsible for selecting the mix proportions to produce the performance *required by the Contract.*

2.   The grade of designed mix concrete is designated by a number, which is the 28 day characteristic compressive strength in N/mmm^2 prefixed by the letter 'C'.

3.   In designing the concrete mixes to be used for the Works the Contractor shall take account of the specified type of cement, maximum and minimum cement contents, nominal maximum sizes of aggregates, and any other imposed conditions *required by the Contract.*

4.   The mix proportions for aqueous liquid retaining structures shall comply with the following:-
   (a)   a minimum cement content of 325 kg/m^3,

   (b)   a maximum cement content of 400 kg/m^3,

   (c)   a maximum water cement ratio of 0.55,

   (d)   a minimum 28 day characteristic cube strength of 35 N/mm^2.

5.   The method of mix design shall be that described in ''Design of Normal Concrete Mixes'', published by Her Majesty's Stationery Office, or other approved method.

6.   The Contractor shall confirm that the designed mixes will produce the required performance by either:-
   (a)   having trial mixes prepared and the subsequent test results, including those from 28 day tests, submitted to the Engineer for approval at least 7 days prior to any particular grade of concrete being used in the Works, or

   (b)   supplying satisfactory evidence that a proposed mix is in continuous production and provides concrete as *required by the Contract.*

7.   Where trial mixes are required:-
   (a)   three separate batches of concrete shall be made using materials typical of the proposed source of supply and, where practicable, under fullscale production conditions,

   (b)   the workability of each of the trial batches shall be determined and three cubes made from each batch for test at 28 days,

   (c)   the trial mix proportions for structural concrete shall be approved if the average compressive strength of the nine cubes tested at 28 days exceeds the required characteristic strength by not less than 10 N/mm^2 for Grade C20 concrete or higher, or 5 N/mm^2 for Grade C15 concrete or lower, provided that the strength determined from any one cube does not fall below the required characteristic strength by more than 1 N/mm^2 or 10%, whichever is the greater,

   (d)   additional sets of cubes from each batch shall be provided for tests at an earlier age, as *required by the Contract*, and

   (e)   two further trial mix batches shall be made with cement and typical surface dry aggregates to show that any stated maximum water cement ratio is not exceeded. The proposed mix proportions shall not be accepted unless both batches have the correct cement content and a water cement ratio below the maximum specified value for the intended degree of workability. For this purpose existing test reports may be used instead of trial mixes if the Engineer is satisfied that the materials to be incorporated in the concrete are likely to be similar to those used in the tests.

8.   Variations in the constituent materials or the proportions of an approved mix shall require approval in writing.

421.   Admixtures

1.   Admixtures or cements containing additives and replacements shall be used only where approved or *required by the Contract*.

2.   If the Contractor seeks approval for the use of an additive he shall provide the Engineer with the following information:-
   (a)   the typical dosage and details of the effects of under and over- dosage,

   (b)   the chemical names of the main active ingredients in the admixture,

   (c)   whether or not the admixture contains chlorides and, if so, the chloride content of the admixture expressed as a percentage of anhydrous calcium chloride by mass of admixture, and

   (d)   whether or not the admixture leads to the entrainment of air when used at the manufacturer's recommended dosage.

3.   All liquid admixtures shall be dispensed by means of an automatic device with a positive method of ensuring that only one dose is dispensed into any one batch.

4.   Calcium chloride or chloride based admixtures shall not be used in concrete containing reinforcement, prestressing tendons, or other embedded metal items.

5.   Pulverised fuel ash shall not be used in conjunction with sulphate resisting cement to BS 4027.

6.   When *required by the Contract*, concrete shall contain an air entraining agent and the average air content by volume of the fresh concrete at the time of placing shall be:-

   7% for 10 mm nominal maximum aggregate size
   6% for 14 mm nominal maximum aggregate size
   5% for 20 mm nominal maximum aggregate size
   4% for 40 mm nominal maximum aggregate size

422.   Delivery and Storage of Materials

1.   Cement shall be stored in a dry weatherproof ventilated shed with a raised wooden floor and suitable ventilation, or in a silo, and shall be delivered in quantities sufficient to ensure that there is no suspension or interruption of the work of concreting at any time. If stored in a shed, each consignment shall be kept separate and distinct. To prevent cement from remaining too long in storage, consignments shall be used in the same order as they are delivered to the site.

2.   All aggregates brought on site shall be kept free from contact with deleterious matter. Aggregates of different sizes, or from different suppliers, shall be stored in different bays, which shall be on a free draining concrete base and separated from each other.

423.   Mixing Concrete

1.   The weighing and water dispensing mechanisms shall be maintained in good order. Their accuracy shall be maintained within the tolerances described in BS 1305 and checked against accurate weights and volumes when directed.

2.   The weights of cement and each size of aggregate as indicated by the mechanisms employed shall be within a tolerance of ± 3% of the respective weights per batch as approved or *required by the Contract*. The weight of the fine and coarse aggregates shall be adjusted to allow for the free water contained in them. The water to be added to the mix shall be reduced by the quantity of free water contained in the fine and coarse aggregates and shall be determined by the Contractor and approved.

3.   Unless otherwise approved, concrete shall be mixed in a batch type mixer manufactured in accordance with BS 1305, or in a batch type mixer, a specimen of which has been tested in accordance with BS 3963 and having a mixing performance within the limits of BS 1305. Where appropriate, the batch capacity, method of loading, mixing time and drum speed, shall conform to the details furnished in accordance with BS 3963 for the mix which corresponds most closely to the mix proportions being used. The mixing blades of pan mixers shall be maintained within the tolerances specified by the manufacturer of the mixer.

4.   Mixers which have been out of use for more than 30 minutes shall be thoroughly cleaned before any fresh concrete is mixed. Mixing plant shall be cleaned thoroughly before changing from one type of cement to another.

5.   The temperature of the water and cement when added to the mix shall each not exceed 60°C.

6.   Concrete shall not be mixed when the air temperature in the shade is below 3°C unless approved cold weather precautions are taken. During cold weather, the following conditions shall apply:-
   (a)   all materials and mixing water shall be free from snow, ice and frost,
   (b)   when the prevailing air temperature is 3°C or lower, means shall be provided to ensure that the temperature of the concrete leaving the mixer is not lower than 10°C, and
   (c)   mixing water when heated to above 32°C, shall be added to the aggregates and then mixed to achieve a uniform temperature before the cement is added.

7.   During hot weather the Contractor shall ensure that the constituent materials of the concrete are sufficiently cool to prevent the concrete from stiffening in the interval between its discharge from the mixer and compaction in its final position. The aggregate stockpiles shall be shielded from the direct rays of the sun or cooled by spraying with water and the mixing water shall be insulated or cooled to ensure that the temperature of the concrete, when placed, shall not exceed 30°C.

424.   Hand Mixing of Concrete
1.   Hand mixing of concrete, if approved shall be done on a hard, clean, impermeable surface, the material being carefully turned over twice in a dry state and three times after the addition of water. Cement shall be increased by 10% in hand mixing and not more than 0.3 m^3 shall be mixed at one time.

425.   Ready-Mixed Concrete
1.   The use of ready-mixed concrete batched off the site and delivered in a plastic condition ready for placing in its final position shall be permitted, provided that:-
   (a)   the constituent materials and the concrete mix shall comply with all the *requirements of the Contract*,
   (b)   the concrete shall be supplied by an approved company and plant which shall operate approved quality systems,
   (c)   water shall be added to the mix only under the control of the central batching unit at the plant, and
   (d)   works test cubes shall be made on the site by the Contractor as *required by the Contract* irrespective of any cubes made by the supplier.

426.   Transport and Placing Concrete
1.   The method of transporting and placing concrete shall be approved. Concrete shall be transported from the mixer and placed in the formwork as rapidly as practicable by methods that will maintain the required workability and will prevent segregation, loss of any ingredients or ingress of foreign matter or water. The concrete shall be deposited as close as practicable to its final position to avoid rehandling or moving the concrete horizontally by vibration.

2. Before placing the concrete, the Contractor shall remove all water and foreign matter from the surface of the formation level or previously placed concrete.

3. Concrete shall not be placed in any part of the structure without approval. If concreting is not started within 24 hours approval shall again be obtained.

4. Concreting shall proceed continuously between joints as *required by the Contract*. Fresh concrete shall not be placed against in situ concrete which has been in position for more than 30 minutes unless a construction joint is formed in accordance with Clause 435. When the in situ concrete has been in place for 4 hours, or less if *required by the Contract*, no further concrete shall be placed against it for a further 20 hours. In the case of vertical joints the minimum period shall be 3 days and for infill panels, 7 days.

5. At the time of placing, concrete shall have a temperature of not less than 5°C and not more than 30°C.

6. Concrete shall not be placed when the air temperature in the shade is below 3°C unless approved cold weather precautions are taken. During cold weather, the following conditions shall apply:-

   (a)   before placing concrete, the formwork, reinforcement and any surfaces with which the fresh concrete will be in contact shall be free from ice, snow and frost, and

   (b)   concreting shall be discontinued when the air temperature in the shade falls below -3°C unless further approved measures are taken to heat the entire area within which concreting is to take place.

7. During hot weather, approved means shall be provided to avoid premature drying out of concrete placed in contact with hot dry surfaces.

8. Concrete shall be compacted in its final position within 30 minutes of discharge from the mixer, unless carried in purpose-made agitators operating continously, when the time shall be within 2 hours of the introduction of the cement to the mix and within 30 minutes of discharge from the agitator.

9. Concrete shall be deposited in horizontal layers to a compacted depth not exceeding 450 mm where internal vibrators are used, or 300 mm in all other cases. The depth of lift to be concreted shall be determined by the Contractor and approved.

10. When trunking or chutes are used they shall be kept clean and used in such a way as to avoid segregation of the mix. Cohesive mixes which do not segregate may be allowed to fall freely provided care is taken to avoid displacement of or damage to reinforcement or formwork.

11. Concrete shall not be placed in flowing water. Under water, concrete shall be placed in position by tremies, or by pipeline from the mixer and never allowed to fall freely through the water. Details of the method proposed shall be approved before placing begins. Where the concrete is placed by a tremie, its size and method of operation shall comply with BS 8004. During and after concreting under water, pumping and dewatering operations in the immediate vicinity shall be suspended until the Engineer permits them to be continued.

12. Water shall not be allowed to flow over or exert any pressure against concrete until at least 48 hours after deposition.

13. Where concrete is to be pumped, details of the methods and plant to be used shall be approved.

427. Compaction of Concrete

1. Concrete shall be thoroughly compacted by vibration or other means during placing, and worked around the reinforcement, tendons or duct formers, embedded fixtures and into corners of the formwork to form a solid, homogeneous, void-free mass having the required surface finish.

2.   When vibrators are used, vibration shall be applied continuously during the placing of each batch of concrete until the expulsion of air has practically ceased and in a manner that does not promote segregation. Over-vibration shall be avoided.

3.   Concrete shall not be subjected to vibration between 4 and 24 hours after compaction.

4.   When external vibrators are used, the design of formwork and disposition of vibrators shall be such as to ensure efficient compaction and to avoid surface blemishes.

5.   Sufficient vibrators in serviceable condition shall be on site so that spare equipment is always available in the event of breakdowns.

428.   Removal of Formwork

1.   The Contractor shall give the Engineer reasonable notice of his intention to strike any formwork. The time at which the formwork is struck shall be the Contractor's responsibility, but the minimum periods between the end of concreting and the removal of forms, shall be as stated in Table 400C.

2.   Days during which the air temperature is below 2°C shall be disregarded in calculating the minimum time which shall elapse before forms are removed.

3.   Formwork shall be removed in an approved manner without shock, vibration or other damage to the concrete.

4.   If approved, the striking time may be decided on the basis of cube strength test results as described in BS 8110.

TABLE 400C Minimum period before striking formwork when using concrete made with ordinary or sulphate resisting Portland cement

Type of formwork	Minimum period before striking		
	Surface temperature of concrete		
	16°C and above	7°C	t at any temperature between 0°C and 25°C
Vertical formwork to columns, walls and large beams	12 h	18 h	$\dfrac{300}{t + 10}$ h
Soffit formwork to slabs	4 days	6 days	$\dfrac{100}{t + 10}$ days
Soffit formwork to beams and props to slabs	10 days	15 days	$\dfrac{250}{t + 10}$ days
Props to beams	14 days	21 days	$\dfrac{360}{t + 10}$ days

NOTE 1:   Where it is not practicable to ascertain the surface temperature of the concrete, air temperature averaged over an appropriate period may be used. In case of vertical formwork the average shall be the mean of air temperature observed at the completion of the pour and the air temperature observed 12 hours later. In the case of other formwork the props the man daily air temperature observed 12 hours later. In the case of other formwork the props, the mean daily air temperature over the appropriate numbers of days be average. Mean daily temperature air temperature over the appropriate number of days shall be averaged. Mean daily temperature shall be taken as the mean of the maximum and minimum air temperature observed each day on a suitably installed maximum/minimum thermometer.

NOTE 2:   For average temperatures between those shown in the table, the minimum period before striking may be obtained by interpolation.

NOTE 3:   For temperatures below 7°C, the tabulated times for soffit formwork shall be increased by half a day for each day on which the concrete temperature was generally between 2°C and 7°C.

NOTE 4:   In the case of vertical formwork, the minimum period shall be extended by 12 hours for each 12 hours that the temperature is between 2°C and 7°C, up to a limit of 48 hours.

429. Curing of Concrete

1. Immediately after compaction, and for a period thereafter not less than that shown in Table 400D, concrete shall be protected from the following:-

(a)   premature drying out, particularly from solar radiation and wind,

(b)   leaching out by rain and flowing water,

(c)   rapid cooling,

(d)   high internal thermal gradients,

(e)   low temperature or frost, and

(f)   vibration or impact which may disrupt the concrete or interfere with its bond to the reinforcement.

During this period, no part of the surface shall fall below a temperature of 5°C nor shall water curing be applied until the concrete reaches a strength of 5 N/mm^2, as confirmed by tests on cubes matured under similar conditions.

TABLE 400D Minimum period of curing and protection

Type of Cement	Ambient conditions after casting	Minimum periods of curing and protection		
		Average surface temperature of concrete		
		5°C to 10°C	Above 10°C	t at any temperture between 5°C and 25°C
OPC, RHPC, SRPC	Average	4 days	3 days	$\dfrac{60}{t + 10}$ days
All except RHPC, OPC and SRPC and all with GGBFS or PFA	Poor / Average	6 days	4 days	$\dfrac{80}{t + 10}$ days
	Poor	40 days	7 days	$\dfrac{140}{t + 10}$ days
All	Good		No special requirements	

NOTE 1:   Abbreviations for the type of cement used are as follows:-
   OPC: ordinary Portland cement see BS 12
   RHPC:rapid hardening Portland cement see BS 12
   SRPC:sulphate resisting Portland cement see BS 4027
   GGBFS:ground granulated blast furnace slag
   PFA:pulverised fuel ash

NOTE 2:   Ambient conditions after casting are as follows:-
   good:damp and protected i.e. relative humidity greater than 80% and protected from sun and wind
   average: intermediate between good and poor
   poor: dry or unprotected i.e. relative humidity less than 50% and not protected from sun and wind.

2. The methods of protection used shall be by one or more of the following, as approved:-

   (a) maintaining formwork in place,

   (b) after thorough wetting, covering the surface with an impermeable material such as polythene, which shall be well sealed and fastened,

   (c) spraying the surface with an efficient non-staining, non-toxic liquid curing membrane which is either self removing or easily removed following the curing period and which has a 75% moisture retention standard or as *required by the Contract,*

   (d) covering the surface with a damp absorbent material, kept constantly wet, or

   (e) continuous or frequent applications of water to the surface, avoiding alternate wetting and drying and the application of cold water to warm concrete surfaces.

3. During cold weather, the required concrete temperatures shall be maintained by one or more of the following as approved:-

   (a) covering the formwork and concrete surfaces with insulating materials,

   (b) shielding newly-placed concrete from the wind,

   (c) using a heated enclosure completely surrounding the newly-placed concrete, avoiding drying of the concrete, or

   (d) using heated formwork panels, avoiding drying of the concrete.

4. Curing membranes which would impair adhesion shall not be used on concrete surfaces which are to be waterproofed, or where laitance is removed and aggregate exposed to provide a satisfactory bond for placing further concrete or mortar screeds.

430. Early Loading

1. Concrete shall at no time be subjected to loading, including its own weight, which will induce a compressive stress in it exceeding 0.33 of its compressive strength at the time of loading or 0.33 of the specified 28 day strength, whichever is the lesser.

2. For the purpose of this Clause, the assessment of the strength of the concrete and the stresses produced by the loads shall be subject to approval.

431. Quality of Finish

1. The quality of finish shall be as *required by the Contract.*

2. If any portion of the concrete face proves unsatisfactory on removal of the formwork it shall, without delay, be cut out and made good as directed. No plastering of concrete surfaces shall be allowed.
If approved, boardmarks or minor discontinuities on exposed faces may be removed by rubbing down with carborundum, and pinholes, small voids or minor porosity of the surface, may be filled by rubbing down with cement and sand mortar of the same proportions as in the concrete. Treatment shall be carried out immediately after removing the formwork.

3. Any concrete, the surface of which has been treated without approval, shall be liable to rejection.

4. The finished surface of water retaining concrete shall not be drilled, punctured by any temporary fixing, or otherwise broken into except as *required by the Contract.*

432. Applied Finishes

1. Where an applied finish is to be used the concrete shall be finished as *required by the Contract.* Approved adhesives and materials shall be applied in accordance with the manufacturer's instructions. Joints in applied finishes shall be made only where directed. After application, remedial treatment other than complete reapplication shall not be permitted on any face.

433. Manufacture of Precast Units

1.   The details of the method of manufacture shall be approved before work is commenced.

2.   Copies of all test results shall be submitted to the Engineer.

3.   In the case of prestressed concrete units, information relating to stressing of the steel shall be provided as *required by the Contract*. The Contractor shall give the Engineer not less than 24 hours notice of stressing, casting and transfer of stress.

4.   Members shall not be despatched to the site until all tests *required by the Contract* have been satisfactorily completed.

5.   Construction tolerances shall comply with BS 8110.

6.   All members shall be indelibly marked on a non-exposed face to show on which production line they were manufactured, the date on which the concrete was cast, the prestress applied and, if they are of symmetrical section, the face which will be uppermost when the member is in its correct position in the Works.

434. Storage, Handling and Placing of Precast Units

1.   The handling and erection of precast units, whether on or off site, shall comply with BS 8110.

2.   When members are stored, they shall be firmly supported at such bearing positions as will ensure that the stresses induced in them are always less than the permissible design stresses.

3.   Members shall be lifted or supported only at the points as *required by the Contract*, and shall be handled and placed without impact.

435. Construction Joints

1.   A construction joint is a joint in the concrete introduced for convenience in construction at which measures are taken to achieve subsequent continuity.

2.   The concrete at the joint shall be bonded with that subsequently placed against it, without provision for relative movement between the two. Concrete shall not be allowed to run to a feather edge, and vertical joints shall be formed against a stop end suitably notched to pass continuous reinforcement.

3.   The surface of the pour shall be roughened to provide aggregate interlock before placing the subsequent pour. In the case of horizontal joints, the joint suface shall be roughened, without disturbing the coarse aggregate particles, by spraying the joint surface approximately 2 to 4 hours after the concrete is placed with a fine spray of water and brushing with a stiff brush. Vertical joints may be treated similarly if the use of retarder on the stop end is approved.

4.   If the joint surface is not roughened until the concrete has hardened, the larger aggregate particles near the surface shall be exposed by sandblasting or by applying a scaling hammer or other mechanical device avoiding damage to edges of the concrete. The joint surface shall be cleaned and dampened immediately before the fresh concrete is placed against it. Dampening is not necessary when an approved bonding agent is used. Particular care shall be taken in the placing of fresh concrete close to the joint to ensure it has an adequate fines content and is fully compacted and dense.

5.   Construction joints shall be positioned as *required by the Contract*. When additional construction joints are required, the Contractor shall submit proposals for the layout and details of them for approval before concreting is started.

436. Movement Joints

1. A movement joint is a specially formed joint intended to accommodate relative movement between adjoining parts of a structure.

2. Movement joints shall be constructed as *required by the Contract*.

3. Any joint filler shall be fixed firmly to the concrete. If more than one strip is used within a joint, the ends shall be butted tightly and taped together.

4. Vertical joints shall be formed against a stop end suitably notched where necessary to pass continous reinforcement. Where stop ends comprise more than one element, joints between elements shall be sufficiently tight to prevent loss of cement grout or fines. If approved, contraction joints may be introduced by the use of proprietory devices.

5. Movement joints shall be protected from the entry of debris prior to sealing.

437. Joint Sealing and Waterstops

1. Where *required by the Contract*, all joint fillers, sealants, waterstops and other proprietory materials shall be used in accordance with the manufacturer's recommendations.

2. Waterstops shall be fully supported in the formwork, without the use of nails and clear of reinforcement or other fixtures. Waterstops shall be clean and free from all water and foreign matter and they shall be fixed so as to ensure that they are not displaced or distorted during compaction of the concrete.

438. Granolithic Concrete

1. Granolithic concrete shall comply with BS 8204.

2. Monolithic construction shall be adopted wherever practicable and the screed shall be laid within 3 hours of placing the base concrete, which shall be clean and be free from laitance. The screed shall have a minimum thickness of 25 mm when laid monolithically and of 50 mm when laid on to hardened concrete.

3. The base concrete, if hardened, shall be thoroughly roughened by mechanical means to expose the aggregate and cleaned. Thereafter it shall be kept damp for not less than 2 days before placing the screed.

4. The screed shall be placed in alternative bays not exceeding 15 m^2 or as *required by the Contract*. The ratio between the sides of the bays shall be as near to 1:1.5 as practicable. If long bays are adopted the maximum specified bay size shall be achieved by saw cutting completely through the thickness of the screed within 24 hours of placing the screed. The edges of the bays shall be vertical and shall abut closely at all joints.

5. Immediately before granolithic is laid, the surface of the base concrete shall be grouted with neat cement grout of a creamy consistency, well brushed in. An approved bonding agent may be used as an alternative to grouting.

6. The mix proportions by weight, shall be one part cement, one part dry fine aggregate, two parts dry coarse aggregate.

7. The water:cement ratio shall be strictly controlled and shall be as low as possible consistent with the proper hydration of the cement and the efficient placing of the screed and shall not exceed 0.4.

8. After granolithic concrete has been laid, the surface shall be trowelled at least 3 times at intervals during the next 6 to 10 hours to produce a hard uniform surface with a high resistance to abrasion. Power floats may be used if approved.

439. No-Fines Concrete

1. No fines concrete shall consist of ordinary portland cement, 20 mm single size coarse aggregate and water. The volumetric aggregate cement ratio shall be 8. The water cement ratio shall be the minimum necessary to ensure that each particle of aggregate is coated evenly with cement grout and shall be fixed after tests to determine the optimum.

2. After mixing, no fines concrete shall be placed immediately on dry formations without prior application of mortar. It shall be lightly rodded or lightly vibrated with a surface plate vibrator to ensure compaction without the cement grout segregating and forming an impervious layer in the base or elsewhere.

3. No fines concrete shall not be placed during rain unless approved precautions have been taken. Immature no fines concrete shall be protected from damage by the elements, vibration or any other cause and shall not be allowed to dry out.

440. Sampling and Testing

1. The sampling, curing of samples and testing of concrete, fresh or hardened, shall comply with BS 5328 and BS 1881.

2. The frequency of sampling shall be as *required by the Contract*.

3. For measurement of slump, site mixed concrete shall be sampled in accordance with BS 1881.

4. In the case of ready mixed concrete, the alternative method of sampling in BS 5328 shall be used. A single sample shall be taken after allowing an initial discharge from the truck of approximately 0.3 m^3. The sample shall be approximately 20 kg mass and shall be collected from the moving stream in a bucket or other suitable container. The sample shall be remixed on a base plate, subdivided into two specimens and each specimen shall be tested for slump. The average of the two slumps shall be the slump for compliance purposes.

5. For assessment of strength, a sample shall be taken from a randomly selected batch of concrete by taking a number of increments in accordance with BS 1881. The samples, wherever practicable, shall be taken at the point of discharge from the mixer or delivery vehicle. Two test specimens shall be prepared from the sample and both specimens shall be laboratory cured under water at 20°C for 28 days. On completion of curing, the specimens shall be tested and the average of the two results shall be taken as the test result.

441. Compliance

1. Concrete shall comply with BS 5238 Clause 16.

2. For Designed Mixes, compliance with the characteristic compressive strength shall be assumed if both the following conditions are met:-
    (a) the average strength determined from any group of four consecutive test results exceeds the specified characteristic strength by:-

    (i) 3 N/mm^2 for concrete of grade C20 and above

    (ii) 2 N/mm^2 for concrete of grade C15 and below, and

    (b) the strength determined from any single test result is not less than the specified characteristic strength minus:-

    (i) 3 N/mm^2 for concrete of grade C20 and above

    (ii) 2 N/mm^2 for concrete of grade C15 and below.

3. The quantity of concrete represented by any group of four consecutive test results shall include the batches from which the first and last samples were taken, together with all intervening batches. When a test result fails to comply with clause 2(b) above, only the particular batch from which the sample was taken shall be at risk.

54

4.   Where compliance is assessed by observation of the batching or from autographic records, the cement content shall not be less than 95% of the specified minimum or more than 105% of the specified maximum. Where compliance is assessed from the results of analysis tests on fresh concrete, the cement content shall not be less than 90% of the specified minimum or more than 110% of the specified maximum.

5.   The workability of the concrete shall be within one of the following limits as appropriate:-

(a)   Slump ± 25 mm or ± 1/3 of the specified value, whichever is the greater.

		Specified value	Tolerance
(b)	Slump with the sample taken by alternative method in Clause 440.4.	25 mm	+ 35 mm − 25 mm
		50 mm	± 35 mm
		75 mm or over	± 1/3 of specified slump plus 10 mm

Limits for intermediate slumps shall be found by interpolation.

6.   For Prescribed Mixes, compliance shall be assumed if observation of the batching or examination of the autographic records of the batch weights used shows that the mix proportions are within ± 5% of the values specified.

442.   Inspection and Testing of Precast Concrete Units
1.   The inspection and testing of precast concrete units shall comply with BS 8110.

443.   Testing Air Entrained Concrete
1.   In air entrained concrete the air content shall be checked at least twice during each pour using an approved air meter. Slump and compaction tests shall be done on the same batch of air entrained concrete as that from which the concrete for the test cubes is taken, but the cubes shall not be made from concrete used in the slump and compaction tests.

444.   Failure to Meet Specified Requirements
1.   If any specified requirement has not been met, the Contractor shall before proceeding with the concreting, submit for approval details of the action which he proposes to ensure that the concrete will comply with the Specification.

445.   Records
1.   The Contractor shall keep up to date records of the positions in the Works of all batches of concrete, their grades, all tests on concrete, the dates and times when concreting was carried out and the weather and temperature conditions at the time. Copies of these records shall be supplied to the Engineer.

446.   Testing of Liquid Retaining Structures
1.   Concrete tanks and other liquid retaining structures shall not be backfilled or built against until the test for liquid retention has been completed. The test shall be carried out in accordance with BS 8007.

2.   After filling, the liquid level shall be maintained by the addition of further liquid for a stabilising period of 7 days or as *required by the Contract*.

3.   After the stabilising period, the level of the liquid surface shall be recorded at 24 hour intervals for a test period of 7 days. During the 7 day test period the total permissible drop in level, after allowing for evaporation and rainfall, shall not exceed 1/500th of the average liquid depth of the full tank, 10 mm or other amount *required by the Contract*.

4.   Notwithstanding the satisfactory completion of the test, seepage and leaks of the liquid to the outside faces of the liquid retaining walls shall be rectified by approved means.

5.   Should the structure not satisfy the 7 day test, then after completion of the remedial work it shall be refilled and undergo a further approved stabilising period. A further test of 7 days duration shall then be undertaken in accordance with this Clause.

6.   For multicompartment structures each compartment shall be tested separately, in addition to any test on the whole structure. The duration of the test on each compartment and permissible drop in level shall be as *required by the Contract*.

7.   The roofs of liquid retaining structures shall be watertight and shall be tested on completion by flooding the roof with water to a minimum depth of 25 mm for a period of 24 hours or as *required by the Contract*.

8.   Where it is impracticable to contain a 25 mm depth of water, the roof shall have water applied continuously to provide a sheet flow of water over the entire area of the roof for a period of not less than 6 hours.

9.   In either case the roof shall be considered satisfactory if no leaks or damp patches show on the soffit.

10.   Should the roof not satisfy the test, then after completion of the approved remedial works, it shall be retested.

447.   Scouring of Structures
1.   Before disinfection all internal surfaces of structures shall be scoured and the structures flushed to remove all foreign matter.

448.   Disinfection of Structures
1.   Where *required by the Contract*, a solution containing 50 mg/l of chlorine and brushed vigorously into the internal surfaces of the structure. The Contractor shall provide goggles and protective clothing for the men doing this work.

2.   A contact period of not less than 30 minutes shall be allowed before flushing the surface with clean water.

3.   The Contractor shall dispose of the waste chlorine solution in such a manner as to avoid the pollution of nature waters, reservoirs and artificial watercourses.

Pipe laying and Jointing

501. Pipelines; General

1. On any section of the works the Contractor shall use pipes and fittings obtained from one manufacturer only unless otherwise approved.

2. 'Rigid joints' shall mean joints made by bolting together flanges integral with the barrels of the pipes, by welding together the barrels of the pipes, by caulking sockets with non-deformable material, such as cement mortar, or by similar techniques.

3. 'Flexible joints' shall mean joints made with factory-made jointing materials, loose collars, rubber rings and the like, which allow some degree of flexing between adjacent pipes.

502. Pipe Trenches; General

1. The requirements of Series 200 read with the particular requirements of this Series shall apply to pipe trenches.

503. Excavation of Pipelines

1. Topsoil shall be stripped, laid aside and kept separate from other excavated materials. Where *required by the Contract* turf shall be stripped by hand and carefully stacked. Road bottoming and surfacing material which is approved as suitable for reuse shall be laid aside and kept separate from other excavated materials.

2. Where *required by the Contract* topsoil shall be stripped over the full or part width of the working area before any other operation is carried out and the soil deposited in stockpiles on Site. On completion of the other operations the subsoil must be broken up and cultivated in accordance with Clause 217 and the topsoil evenly spread over the prepared surface and lightly compacted.

3. Trenches for pipes, other than those for field or French drains, shall be excavated to a sufficient depth and width, subject to the restriction in Clause 503.4, to enable the pipe, joint, bed, haunch and surround to be accommodated.

4. The width of trenches shall comply with Table 500A up to a minimum of 300 mm above the top of the pipe barrel. Battering the sides of trenches shall be permitted only above this level and where approved.

Table 500A Trench Width

Nominal Internal Diameter of Pipe *mm*	Minimum Trench Width *mm*	Maximum Trench Width *mm*
100	430	630
150	490	690
225	580	780
300	680	880
375	950	1 150
450	1 030	1 230
525	1 120	1 320
600	1 240	1 440
675	1 330	1 530
750	1 400	1 600
825	1 490	1 690
900	1 920	2 120
1 050	2 100	2 300
1 200	2 290	2 490
Above 1 200	Outside diameter of pipe plus 800 mm	Outside diameter of pipe plus 1 000 mm

All sheeting and supports are to be outwith the minimum width.
The maximum width includes an allowance for sheeting and tolerance.

5.   Should the specified maximum width be exceeded due to the Contractor's method of working he shall provide whatever approved additional pipe protection is necessary.

6.   Where rock or boulders are present in pipe trenches the sides of the trenches shall be so trimmed that when the pipe is laid to the correct level and alignment no projection of rock comes within 100 mm of the outside of the pipe at any point.

7.   Where rock occurs at the level to which pipes are to be laid the bottom of the trench shall be further excavated to provide a clearance between the pipe barrel and the rock of one quarter of the outside diameter of the pipe subject to a minimum clearance under pipe and sockets of 150 mm and maximum 400 mm.

8.   Trenches for pipes under pressure shall be excavated to a sufficient depth to ensure, after consolidation of the refilling, a normal minimum depth of cover of 900 mm from the ground surface to the top of the pipe. Where the pipeline is required to be laid to a depth which does not permit this condition to be fulfilled the ground surface shall be made up locally with banking.

9.   The Contractor shall fill up any excessive depth of trench arising from his method of working with well compacted Type A granular bedding material to Clause 341, or with concrete Grade C7.5P to Clause 419 where directed.

10.   Where the trench formation is in ground that, in the opinion of the Engineer, is unsuitable to afford proper support to the pipes, either
   (a)   the trench shall be excavated down to solid ground and the extra depth shall be refilled with Grade C7.5P concrete to Clause 419, type A granular bedding material, gravel or broken stone, as directed, well compacted to form an even bed, or

   (b)   the pipes shall be supported by a geotextile system, piles or such other means as directed.

11.   The Contractor shall avoid unduly disturbing the finished trench formation and shall make good disturbed areas and excavate any wet or puddled material. Voids shall be made good as in Clause 503.10(a).

12.   Trenches close to existing structures shall be opened in short lengths and refilled as *required by the Contract*.

13.   The material excavated in forming pipe trenches shall if unsuitable as backfill in accordance with Clause 209.2 be replaced with selected fill type B. Suitable material shall be set aside and protected for use as backfill.

14.   All surplus excavated material shall be disposed of in accordance with Clause 201.5.

504.   Pipelaying; General
1.   Flat braided steel wire slings or band slings shall be used for slinging all pipes except externally coated pipes and plastic pipes for which only special band slings not less than 300 mm wide shall be used. Chain or rope slings, hooks or other devices working on scissor or grab principles shall not be used.

2.   Subject to the requirements of inspection before acceptance, protective bolsters, caps or discs on the ends of flanges or pipes, specials or fittings shall not be removed until the pipes, specials, or fittings are about to be lowered into the trench.

3.   Before a pipe is lowered into the trench, it shall be thoroughly examined to ensure that the internal coating or lining and the outer coating or sheathing are undamaged. Where necessary the interiors of pipes, specials and fittings shall be brushed clean. Any damaged parts of the coatings or linings shall, before a pipe is used, be made good in accordance with the manufacturer's instructions.

4.   Pipelaying shall not commence until the bottom of the trench and the pipe bed have been approved.

5.   Flexible pipes, rigidly jointed, may be joined on the ground surface before lowering into the trench. All joints shall be supported by slings as the pipes are lowered and the pipeline shall not be deformed to a greater extent than that recommended by the manufacturer.

6.   Pipes shall be brought to the correct alignment and inclination, concentric with the pipes already laid.

7.   All pipes shall be sorted, handled, laid and jointed in accordance with the manufacturer's instructions and where appropriate at his recommended temperatures.

8.   If entry to pipes by workmen and materials is required the Contractor shall provide such equipment, clothing and footwear as in the opinion of the Engineer will not damage any lining to the pipes.

505. Withdrawal of Supports

1.   During the placing of bedding, haunching, surrounding or anchoring material temporary side supports and sheeting shall be removed progressively except where directed to be left in and the full width of the trench shall be infilled with bedding, haunching, surrounding or anchoring materials, care being taken to fill all spaces left by withdrawn sheeting and framing.

506. Bedding and Protecting Pipes

1.   A cavity of adequate size shall be excavated in the sides and bottom of the trench or left in the pipe bed at each joint and at each sling position.

2.   The bottom of the trench or surface of the bed shall be finished to a smooth even surface at the correct levels to permit the barrel of the pipe to be solidly and evenly bedded throughout its whole length between joint and sling holes.

3.   Preparation of the trench bottom or surface of the bed shall be completed for at least one full pipe length in advance of the pipelaying, except where another arrangement is approved.

4.   No bedding material shall be placed in trenches containing water.

5.   Where granular bedding is to be used, stones, bricks or similar materials shall not be used below or against the pipes to locate them in position in the trench or to level the pipes. Sufficient of the infill materials shall be placed around the barrels of pipes to prevent movement.

6.   Where required in order to comply with Clause 523 or Clause 524 the method of haunching and surrounding pipes shall be modified to leave joints exposed.

7.   Material in bedding, haunching and surrounds to pipes shall be compacted in layers not exceeding 150 mm thick before compaction.

8.   Where material is to be placed compaction of material shall proceed equally on both sides of the pipe.

9. Where concrete bedding, haunching or surround is used backfilling of the trench shall not be commenced until the concrete has reached a strength of 15 N/mm^2.

10. Before placing concrete, pipes shall be supported near joints on a precast concrete block or engineering bricks with a padding of two layers of hessian based damp proof course or material of similar yield between the barrel of the pipe and the supporting block. The surface of the support shall be perfectly smooth for at least 75 mm by 75 mm under the pipe, and the size of the block shall be as *required by the Contract*.

11. Concreting of bedding, haunches or surrounds shall not be done until the pipes have been jointed and inspected. The concrete shall be vibrated into place under the pipe and shall be in full contact with the underside of the barrel of the pipe throughout its length. The concrete shall be placed in one operation and shall be well worked to form a homogeneous mass. There shall be no horizontal construction joint in the concrete below the level of the half pipe. The pipe shall be carefully anchored against flotation.

12. Concrete bedding, haunching or surrounding pipes shall be discontinuous at flexible pipe joints. Shaped formwork shall be provided and left at pipe joints as *required by the Contract*. It shall be made from fibreboard or other equally compressible material of thickness not less than one per cent of the pipe length with a maximum of 35 mm unless otherwise directed. The formwork shall be of size or shape equal to the net section of the concrete protection to the pipe and shall be neatly cut and properly supported by temporary struts and rails where necessary.

13. Plastic pipes shall be wrapped in polythene sheet or roofing felt with a minimum thickness of 2 mm before being haunched or anchored in concrete.

14. Concrete in pipe anchorages and thrust blocks shall be Grade C 20P/20 to Clause 419. These items shall not be subjected to loading until the concrete has reached a strength of 15 N/mm^2.

15. Concrete in pipe anchorages and thrust blocks in trench shall be placed against undisturbed ground. Any loose or disturbed material shall be removed immediately before the concrete is placed.

16. Concrete anchorages to uPVC pipes shall be placed to support half the circumference of the pipe. The pipe shall not be encased. Where compliance with this requirement would result in concrete above the pipe, the anchorage concrete shall be placed beneath the pipe and the pipe shall be restrained by straps as *required by the Contract*.

17. Where pressure pipelines are not buried in the ground the exposed pipes shall be lagged with fully flexible closed cell elastomeric insulation or glass fibre rigid sections 25 mm thick covered with polyisobutylene sheets not less than 0.8 mm thick sealed by solvent or cold welding. All lagging shall extend at least 1 m into the trench at either end.

507. Plugs

1. Immediately after laying, the open end of a pipe shall be sealed with an approved stopper to prevent the entry of anything which might contaminate or damage the pipeline or affect its operation.

2. The plugs in sewers may, if approved, be provided with small holes for drainage purposes, but water from the trench excavation which is heavily charged with silt shall not be allowed to gain access to the pipeline.

3. Where work is interrupted for a period, the plugs left in position shall be regularly inspected to ensure that they have not been disturbed. Whenever any plug is removed, the immediate length of pipe shall be examined for dirt or obstructions and shall be cleaned as required.

4. Adequate precautions shall be taken, by way of backfilling or other means, to anchor each pipe securely to prevent flotation of the pipeline in the event of the trench being flooded.

5. On completion of the Works the Contractor shall hand over sewers and pipelines in a clean condition, free from deposits.

508. Gaps for Valves and Specials

1.   If the normal continuity of construction requires to be interrupted pending the delivery of valves or specials, the exact extent of the temporary gaps to be left shall be predetermined after reference to the Engineer. The Contractor shall submit dimensioned sketches to the Engineer for approval, showing details of the pipe and jointing arrangements to be adopted to effect ultimate closure. Care shall be taken to preserve the accurate alignment of the pipeline across all such temporary gaps.

509. Jointing Pipes; General

1.   Joints shall be made in accordance with the manufacturer's instructions. The Contractor shall make use of the technical advisory services offered by manufacturers for instructing pipe jointers in the methods of assembling joints. Where manufacturers recommend the use of special jointing tackles, the Contractor shall use these for assembly of all joints.

2.   Before making any joints, all jointing surfaces shall be thoroughly cleaned and dried and maintained in such condition until the joints have been completely made or assembled.

3.   Notwithstanding any flexibility provided in the pipe joints, pipes must be securely positioned to restrict movement during and after the making of the joint.

4.   The space between the end of the spigot and the shoulder of the socket of flexibly jointed pipes shall be as recommended by the manufacturer or as *required by the Contract*.

5.   Where loose collars are used to join pipes, special tools shall be employed to keep the inside of the pipes flush and the collar concentric with the pipe while the joint is being made.

510. Flanged Joints

1.   The flanges shall be correctly positioned and the component parts including any insertion ring cleaned and dried. Insertion rings shall be fitted smoothly to the flange without folds or wrinkles. The face and bolt holes shall be brought fairly together and the joints made by gradually and evenly tightening bolts in diametrically opposed positions. Bolts shall be finally tightened by application of the maximum torque appropriate to the type and diameter of bolt. The protective coating, if any, of the flange shall be made good when the joint is completed.

511. Fusion Jointing of Polyethylene Pipes

1.   Fusion welded joints in high density and medium density polyethylene pipes shall be made only between pipes having the same physical characteristics. Joints between pipes from different manufacturers shall be made only where approved.

2.   The pipe section containing the completed weld shall have at least the same strength as the original pipe.

3.   When welds are made during inclement weather suitable protection shall be provided to ensure that constant temperature conditions are maintained at the joint.

4.   Joints shall be made in accordance with the guidance notes of manufacturers and the current edition of the WRc Manual for MDPE Pipe Systems for Water Supply.

512. Protection of Pipes and Joints

1.   Polythene sleeve for ductile iron pipes shall be a minimum 1000 gauge thickness and shall be of such diameter that it will pass easily over the socket. The sleeve will be fixed in position in accordance with the pipe manufacturer's instructions.

2. Joints having exposed mild steel components shall be cleaned and protected by one of the following methods:-

(a) The application of approved mastic paste in sufficient quantity to cover all protruding edges, bolt heads and sharp edges of flanges, so as to give a smooth external profile, followed by wrapping with two separate layers of approved protective tape wound spirally with a half width overlap. The taping shall extend along 150 mm of the barrel of the pipe on each side of the joint.

(b) The application of a self adhesive rubber based cold applied tape wrap combined with a thick PVC backing. Where bolt heads, flanges and other projections arise a moulding putty shall be used to give a smooth external profile, followed by wrapping with two separate layers of protective tape wrap spirally applied with 50% overlap. The tape shall overlap the existing mill applied coating by 150 mm on each side of the joint.

(c) Painting of the external surface as *required by the Contract*.

513. Laying to Curves

1. Where flexibly jointed pipes are to be laid to curves, this shall be done in accordance with the manufacturer's recommendations.

514. Cutting Pipes

1. Iron pipes shall be cut by a method which provides a clean square cut without damage to pipe or lining. All cut or trimmed ends and any damaged areas of coating shall be recoated with bitumen before the pipes are laid. The external area at cut spigot ends of ductile iron shall be ground for a distance of at least 125 mm.

2. Asbestos cement pipes shall be cut by approved means to a square and even finish without splitting or fracturing the wall of the pipe. A percentage of the pipes ordered shall be supplied with fully turned barrels and these pipes shall be set aside for use in cutting specific lengths. When no fully turned pipes are available a hand operated turning machine shall be used to prepare the ends of cut pipes.

3. MDPE and uPVC pipes shall be cut square by approved means. All burrs shall be removed. The plain end of uPVC pipes shall be chamfered at an angle of 15° to not greater than half the wall thickness of the pipe.

4. Concrete pipes shall be cut to a square and even finish without splitting or fracturing the wall of the pipe. Reinforcement shall be cut back flush with the concrete and bare metal protected with bituminous paint or cement grout as directed.

515. Backfilling of Trenches

1. If the Contractor allows excavated material to become unsuitable for use in backfilling he shall remove it from the Site and replace it with Type B fill.

2. Backfilling shall be undertaken immediately the specified operations preceding it have been completed.

3. No backfill material shall be placed in trenches containing water.

4. In trenches in roads, verges and where *required by the Contract*, above 300 mm over the crown of the pipe backfill material shall be deposited in layers compacted as specified in Clause 212. Power rammers, vibrating plate compactors or vibrating rollers shall be used to compact the backfill from 500mm above the crown level of the pipe to the surface.

5. In trenches in fields or open country backfill material above 300 mm over the crown of the pipe may be placed by machine, provided that material does not drop from a height and that compaction is carried out as *required by the Contract*.

6.   Sufficient space shall be left to receive the original thickness of soil, turf or other materials removed from the surface. The surfaces shall be restored in their proper order by compacting them to ensure that after settlement the surface level is within 30 mm of that of the adjacent undisturbed ground.

7.   Where directed trenches shall be backfilled with lean mix concrete made with 1 kg cement to 12 kg aggregate. The aggregate shall comply with Clause 304.

8.   Temporary reinstatement of streets shall be carried out as *required by the Contract* and in compliance with the requirements of the relevant Highway Authority.

516.   Existing Land Drains
1.   Land drains shall be restored in accordance with Clause 216.

517.   Field and French Drains
1.   Trenches for drains up to 150 mm dia. shall be excavated to a width of at least four times the nominal dia. of the pipe, above 150 mm dia. the width shall be the diameter plus 450 mm.

2.   Where *required by the Contract* pipes for drains shall be bedded on a 75 mm thickness of Grade C 7.5P concrete to Clause 419 which shall be brought up until at least one third of the depth of the pipe is supported and in the case of perforated pipes, no line of perforations is thereby blocked. Non circular pipes shall be bedded as *required by the Contract*.

3.   Socketed pipes shall be laid with a space of about 23 mm between the spigot and the inner end of the socket. Perforated clay pipes with rebated joints shall be dry jointed.

4.   Trenches for French drains shall be backfilled with Type E material in accordance with Clause 342.5 or other filling material *required by the Contract*.

5.   Unless otherwise *required by the Contract* Type E fill material to French drains shall be terminated 75 mm below final level and turfed over.

6.   The pipes, filter material and the surface over drains shall be kept free of obstructions.

518.   Connections to Sewers
1.   Pipe connections to a brick sewer, concrete culvert, stone built or lined channel shall be built in cement mortar into the main sewer drain or channel and shall discharge in the direction of the flow. The ends of pipes shall be cut to the necessary angle. Where connections are between pipe sewers or drains, approved special connection pipes, or precast concrete or vitrified clay saddles sloped to the curvature of the pipe shall be used, unless otherwise *required by the Contract*. All junctions are to be set at the correct angle to minimise the use of bends.
In making connections the Contractor shall take precautions to prevent the entry of debris or any other material into the existing sewers, drains and manholes and shall preserve free flow therein.

2.   The open ends of all house connections and other pipes not required for immediate use shall be sealed up. The positions of the connections and junction shall be marked by posts and painted boards of an approved type and size. Boards shall be marked with the letter 'S' and the size and depth below kerb of the pipe or ground level. A length of 5 mm dia. galvanised iron wire shall be fixed to the faucet of the last pipe and the marking post. Care shall be taken to prevent the marking boards being disturbed. The information shall also be painted on the kerbs in an approved manner when all works are complete, and the Contractor shall record the position of all branches from the manhole immediately downstream.

519.   Pipes Built Into Structures
1.   The outside surfaces of all pipes and special castings to be built into structures shall be cleaned immediately before installation. Where directed protective coatings to metal pipes shall be removed

64

from the sections to be built in and the external surfaces of vitrified clay and concrete pipes shall be roughened to form a key for concrete or mortar. Sheathing to steel pipes shall be cut away from the sections to be built in and after erection approved bituminous material shall be applied around the barrels of pipes at the junctions with structures.

2.   Pipes passing through water retaining walls and floors shall be built into the structure in situ. Shuttering shall be formed closely to the outside of the pipe, and concrete shall be placed and compacted thoroughly round pipe and puddle flange.

3.   Where fixing in the course of construction is not possible, temporary openings in structures shall be provided where *required by the Contract,* or directed, to accommodate the subsequent erection of pipes and special castings. In water retaining structures, they shall taper to a smaller dimension towards the external faces of structures and shall include where *required by the Contract* a waterstop. In basements and dry chambers at pumping stations temporary openings shall taper to a smaller dimension towards the internal faces of structures and shall include where *required by the Contract* a waterstop.

4.   Prior to infilling, surfaces against which fresh concrete is to be placed shall be prepared as specified in Clause 435. The external surfaces of pipework shall be prepared as described in Clause 519.1.

5.   Where flexibly jointed pipelines of concrete, vitrified clay or asbestos cement are to be built into manholes or chambers the first pipe joint outside the manhole must be within 500 mm of the outside face and the next pipe shall not exceed 1 m in length.

520. Setting Valves

1.   Care shall be taken to prevent damage to valves, fire hydrants and the like and their ancillary equipment. Valves and ancillary apparatus shall be stored in clean conditions and in a manner that excludes all water. Electrical equipment shall be protected from damp and damp proofing seals shall remain intact until the electrician is ready to connect up the equipment.

2.   The faces and seats of valves and the cavity beneath the valve door shall be kept clean. If cleaning is required this shall be done by hand.

3.   Valves shall be set so that operating spindles are truly vertical unless otherwise *required by the Contract* or directed.

4.   Before each valve is put into service, gears, bearings and spindles shall be oiled with an approved oil as recommended by the valve maker. Oil baths shall be topped up to the appropriate levels and grease nipples charged with grease of approved manufacture.

5.   Air valves shall not be kept upside down so as to expose the balls and air cavities before installation. Air valves shall be checked for damage before the main is charged.

6.   Fire hydrants, frost plugs and similar fittings shall be checked before the main is charged.

7.   The installation of special types of valve and metering equipment shall be strictly in accordance with the manufacturer's instructions.

521. Cleaning Sewers

1.   Immediately before being handed over to the Employer non pressure sewers shall be cleaned and pipes not exceeding 400 mm dia. shall be flushed with clean water while being rodded from manhole to manhole with a rubber tipped plunger the same size as the bore of the pipe. Manholes, chambers, tanks and sumps shall be washed down, emptied and left to dry.

2.   The bore, linearity and jointing of completed lengths of drains and service ducts less than 300 mm dia. shall be checked by drawing through a mandrel 750 mm long and 12 mm less in diameter than the nominal bore of the pipe or by another approved method.

522. Tolerances

1.   The position of the internal face of any pipeline or manhole, shall be within the following permissible deviations:-

		Permissible deviations
Pipeline	line	± 12 mm
	level	± 12 mm
Shaft verticality		1 in 300

These deviations will be permitted provided they are attained gradually over a length of not less than 10 m and no backfalls result.

2.   The location of any manhole may be departed from on the line of the pipeline to the nearest pipe length or by 600 mm, whichever is the lesser, and by a maximum of 150 mm transversely.

523. Testing Sewers

1.   Testing shall be carried out between manholes. Short branch sewers shall be tested as one system with the main sewer. Long branches shall be tested separately.

2.   Pipes not exceeding 750 mm nominal internal diameter shall be tested in one of the following ways:-

(a)   Water Test

A test pressure of 1.2 m head of water above the soffit of the sewer shall be applied at the high end by means of a standpipe. The length of the section under test shall be such that the head at the lower end does not exceed 6 m. A period of 1 hour shall be allowed for absorption. The loss of water over a period of 30 minutes shall be measured by adding water at regular intervals of 10 minutes. The average quantity of water added shall not exceed 0.1 litre per hour per 100 lineal m/mm of nominal bore of the sewer.

(b)   Air Test

The length of sewer under test shall be effectively plugged and air pumped in until a pressure of 100 mm head of water is indicated in a U-tube connected to the system. The air pressure shall not fall to less than 75 mm head of water during a period of 5 minutes, without further pumping, after a period of stabilisation.

3.   Sewers shall be tested:-
   (a)   after laying, including the placing of concrete if any, but before backfilling, and

   (b)   after backfilling has been completed.

4.   Sewers designed for high pressure shall be tested in accordance with the provisions of Clause 524.

5.   Pipes exceeding 750 mm nominal dia. shall be tested as *required by the Contract*.

6.   Sewers shall be tested for infiltration after backfilling. All inlets to the system shall be effectively closed and the residual flow shall be deemed to be infiltration. The amount of infiltration shall not exceed 0.1 litre per hour per 100 lineal m/mm of nominal bore of the sewer.

7.   Infiltration to manholes shall not exceed 5 litres per hour per manhole.

524. Testing Pressure Pipelines

1.   Pipelines shall be tested hydraulically in sections during the course of construction.

2.   Testing shall be applied to prove the structural soundness of the various units in the line, including pipes, valves and anchorages and to prove the watertightness of the line.

3.   The Contractor shall provide all materials and apparatus necessary for carrying out the tests and shall keep them in good order. Gauges shall be tested to the satisfaction of the Engineer.

4.   The Contractor shall provide for transmitting unsupported end thrusts to solid ground at the ends or into the sides of trenches. Before testing, he shall ensure that the anchorage of bends is complete and that all branch outlets taking end thrust are properly stayed.

5.   Testing shall not be permitted against a closed valve. In-line valves shall be left open. Terminal valves, hydrants, scour valves and the isolating valves of air valves shall be open, and shall be fitted with blank flanges except that where air valves are already fitted they shall be in service during the test. Scour pipes shall be connected only after pipeline testing is complete.

6.   Water required for filling and testing the main shall be obtained from an approved source. Where a supply is taken from an existing main the Contractor shall supply and fit an approved double check valve in the connecting pipe.

7.   The Contractor shall give the Engineer not less than twenty four hours notice of his intention to test a section of the main.

8.   The test pressures shall be as *required by the Contract* for the various sections of the Permanent Works.

9.   When testing, the pipeline shall be charged with water and all air released. Care shall be taken during the charging of the mains to provide free outlets for air to prevent surging and water hammer. The pipeline shall then be brought up to and maintained at operating pressure and left for a period of not less than 24 hours to allow absorption and achieve stable conditions. Thereafter water shall be added by pumping until the test pressure is reached, when the pump shall be isolated. If a drop in pressure occurs, the pump shall be reconnected and the quantity of water added to restore the test pressure shall be measured. This procedure shall be repeated at regular intervals for a period of 2 hours. For steel or prestressed concrete pipes the test pressure may be maintained by continual pumping, and a pressure relief valve, the rate of loss of water being determined at regular intervals during the test period. The amount of water added or lost shall not exceed 0.1 litre per mm nominal internal dia. per kilometre length of main per 30 m head for each twenty four hours. If a test fails it shall be repeated until the specified degree of watertightness is obtained.

10.   Interim tests shall be applied to sections of continuous pipelines in lengths not exceeding 1000 m. After the satisfactory completion of the first sectional test this length may, at the Engineer's discretion, be increased to 1500 m. The first sectional interim test shall be carried out after bedding of the pipeline and backfilling to provide 300 mm depth of material over the crown of the pipe, the tops of all joints being left exposed.
Subsequent interim tests may, at the discretion of the Engineer, be carried out with the trench backfilled except for the replacement of soil or turf.

11.   Each completed continuous length of pipeline shall be subject to a final test as a whole or such parts of the whole as *required by the Contract*.

12.   In the case of short sleeved welded joints on steel pipes, a porosity test to each joint shall be applied by the Contractor under an air pressure of 40 m head of water. Testing shall be carried out as work on pipelaying and backfilling of trenches proceeds. The joint shall be acceptable provided there is no loss in the applied pressure over a period of 30 minutes. A tapped hole for the test connection shall be provided at the socket end of each pipe and a sealing run of welding

added at the face of the socket. On completion of the pipeline, the hydraulic test described in Clause 524.9 shall be applied and, if satisfactory, shall be deemed to satisfy the tests described in Clause 524.10.

13.   The Contractor shall ensure that no erosion, silting or contamination occurs in water courses from the discharge of test water.

525.   Swabbing and Scouring of Pipelines
1.   The Contractor shall swab pressure pipelines with foam swabs in sections as directed. Foam swabs will be provided by the Engineer.

2.   Swabbing shall be continued until the washwater runs clear and the Contractor shall ensure that no erosion, silting or contamination occurs in the watercourses into which the wash water is discharged.

526.   Disinfection of Water Mains
1.   Mains shall be disinfected after testing, swabbing and scouring.

2.   Chlorine solution shall be applied at the charging point as the main is being filled and dosing shall be continued until the main is full and at least 50 mg/l of free chlorine have been made available. Chlorine gas shall not be injected direct to the main from a cylinder otherwise than through an approved chlorinator and care shall be taken to ensure that there is no flow back into the preceding sections of main.

3.   The treated water shall be left in the main for a period as directed but not less than 24 hours and all valves in the system shall be operated at least once during this period.

4.   Chlorine residual tests shall then be taken at the end of the main furthest from the point of injection. The disinfection procedure shall be repeated until the chlorine residual is not less than 10 mg/l.

5.   The Contractor shall dispose of the waste chlorine solution in such a manner as to avoid the pollution of natural waters and of reservoirs and artificial watercourses. The Contractor shall comply with any directions which the Engineer makes in respect of such disposal.

6.   The Contractor shall refill the mains with clean water and leave full to allow samples to be taken by the Water Authority for bacteriological tests. If the results of these tests are unsatisfactory the Contractor shall repeat the disinfection procedure.

527.   Testing of Pipe Bedding Material
1.   The following apparatus shall be used:-
    (a)   Open ended cylinder 254 mm long and 150 mm dia.
    (b)   Metal rammer with a striking face 38 mm dia. and of total weight 1 kg.

2.   Stand the cylinder on a firm flat surface. Using a sample of material having a moisture content equal to that of the material at the time of use, pour the sample of material into the cylinder without supplementary compaction and strike off the material level with the top of the cylinder. Lift the cylinder clear of its contents and place on a fresh area of flat surface. Replace about one quarter of the material in the cylinder and tamp vigorously until no further compaction is evident. Repeat this process quarter by quarter until the whole of the material measured loose in the cylinder is compacted.

3.   The final measurement from the top of the cylinder to the compacted surface divided by the height of the cylinder is the compaction factor value.

Manholes and Chambers

601. Manholes, General

1. Pipes into and out of manholes shall be as short as practicable. They shall be built in monolithically and the manhole made watertight. The pipe ends projecting beyond the manhole walls shall be surrounded by Grade C10P concrete to Clause 419 150 mm thick. Where line, level and pipe diameter permit, the pipeline may be laid unbroken through the manhole position subject to the pipe joints external to the manhole not being more than 500 mm from the outside face of the manhole wall. The pipe within the manhole position shall be cut by approved means to remove the top half wihout damaging the lower half which will form the invert of the channel.

2. Where the pipes in manholes are of different diameters they shall be laid so that the soffits of all pipes are at the same level. The depth of the channel shall be not less than the diameter of the pipe and the invert of the channel shall be formed to an even gradient. Main channel inverts for pipes up to and including 300 mm dia. may be preformed channels of approved material. Main channel inverts for pipes over 300 mm dia. may be as the foregoing or may be formed in granolithic concrete, to Clause 438, trowelled smooth.

3. Branch bends up to and including 150 mm dia. shall be of approved material of half section curved in the direction of flow in the main channel and set so that the invert of the bend within the manhole is at the same gradient as the incoming pipe. Branch bends over 150 mm dia. shall be curved in the direction of flow and shall be formed in granolithic concrete, to Clause 438, trowelled smooth. Spaces between branch bends shall be completely filled with concrete and the faces above the main and branch channel inverts shall be trowelled smooth.

4. Bases of manholes shall be set on blinding concrete Grade C7.5P to Clause 419, 75 mm minimum thickness. Bases and benching shall be formed in concrete Grade C20P to Clause 419. Benching shall be rendered in granolithic concrete to Clause 438, 50 mm thick, trowelled smooth and shall slope at 1 in 12 towards the main channel.

5. Manhole covers and frames shall be fixed in position with the frames solidly bedded in Class M1 cement mortar to Clause 339 so that the covers, when in position, are fair and even with the adjacent surfaces. At least one and not more than three courses of brickwork shall be provided between the cover slab and the manhole frame.

6. Step irons shall not be provided where the depth to benching is less than 900 mm and the largest pipe is less than 450 mm dia.

7. Channels more than 450 mm in depth shall have one or more step irons in a recess 600 mm wide by 150 mm deep with a handrail or post within easy reach.

8. A manhole shaft, excluding 1 to 3 courses of brickwork under the cover, shall not be constructed unless its depth will exceed 1 m.

9. Where the depth from ground level to the top of benching exceeds 2.5 m a ladder shall be used instead of step irons. Manhole ladders shall be constructed as described in Clause 335 and the brackets shall be built into or bolted to the brickwork or concrete.

10. In deep manholes suitable rest chambers shall be provided at about 6 m intervals, each with a landing platform incorporating a hinged trap door immediately under the ladder as *required by the Contract*.

11. Cover slabs and beams of manholes shall be reinforced as *required by the Contract*. The minimum cover to the steel shall be 25 mm and the concrete shall be Grade C30P to Clause 419.

12. All manholes on sewers of 600 mm dia. and over shall be provided with safety chains for placing across the mouth of the sewer on the downstream side when the men are at work and 25 mm dia. solid bar handrail shall be provided on the edges of all benching and platforms.

70

602. Manholes, Brickwork

1. Brick manholes for sewers of 150 mm to 750 mm dia. shall be constructed as *required by the Contract* using Class B engineering bricks, laid in English Bond. Beds and vertical joints shall be completely filled with mortar as the bricks are laid. Joints shall be flush pointed as the work proceeds.

2. Where built into manhole walls pipes of 225 mm to 375 mm dia. shall have two half brick ring relieving arches turned over to the full thickness of the brickwork. Above this size the number of half brick relieving arches shall be increased to three. Walls of manholes of up to 3 m deep below ground level shall be constructed in 225 mm brickwork. Walls of manholes over 3 m deep shall be as *required by the Contract*. Overall manhole dimensions may be adjusted to the nearest half brick size if approved.

3. Manhole shafts shall be 750 mm by 675 mm and where ladders are used this size shall be increased to 900 mm by 675 mm with the shaft top corbelled as necessary.

4. Step irons having a tail 230 mm long shall be built in at 300 mm vertical intervals, as *required by the Contract*, with the uppermost step iron from 400 mm to 600 mm from the top of the manhole cover. Where ladders are used the top rung shall be similarly located.

603. Manholes, In Situ Concrete

1. Details and dimensions of manholes of in situ concrete shall be as for brick manholes using mass concrete Grade C30P to Clause 419.

604. Manholes, Precast Concrete

1. Precast concrete manholes for sewers of 150 mm to 1125 mm shall be constructed as *required by the Contract* using precast concrete components complying with BS 5911 set on a base formed of in situ concrete. The lowest chamber ring shall be bedded on and haunched with cement mortar. The cover slab shall be bedded on the topmost ring on cement mortar. The remaining faces of the joints of chamber rings, taper pieces and shaft rings shall be liberally coated with approved bituminous material of trowelling grade prior to being fixed in position. Any surplus bituminous compound shall be neatly struck off. Alternatively, joints may be sealed with an approved preformed jointing strip applied in accordance with the manufacturer's instructions.

2. Lifting holes in precast units shall be cleaned and filled with cement mortar. Step irons shall not be used for hoisting or lowering components.

3. Where the depth, from ground level or ultimate ground level whichever is the higher, to the base of the precast concrete chamber rings, exceeds 4.5 m, the precast concrete chamber rings shall be surrounded below this depth with Grade C20P concrete to Clause 419 of 150 mm minimum thickness.

4. Step irons having tails 80 mm long shall be built in at 300 mm vertical intervals as *required by the Contract*, and where the tails project they shall be protected by cement mortar.

605. Chambers

1. Chambers for access to valves and fittings on pressure pipelines for water or sewage shall be one of the following:-
   (a) precast concrete sections which shall be interlocking, reinforced as *required by the Contract* and capable of adjustment to the required height. Precast concrete units shall be bedded on well compacted granular material Type A to Clause 341 brought up from the base of the trench, or
   (b) where the chamber required is such that precast concrete units cannot conveniently be used it shall be constructed in brickwork in the manner detailed in Clause 602.

2. Covers and frames shall be fixed in position with the frames solidly bedded in Class M1 cement mortar to Clause 339 so that the covers, when in position, are fair and even with the adjacent surfaces.

Builderwork

701. Brickwork and Blockwork, General

1. Brickwork and blockwork shall comply with BS 5628. The courses shall be properly levelled, perpendiculars kept and quoins, jambs and other angles plumbed as the work proceeds. Corners and other advanced work shall not be raised more than 1.2m above the general level and shall be raked back. For facing brick the whole lift shall be completed in one operation. Advanced work shall be plumbed and the height checked with a gauge rod.

2. Brickwork one brick thick and over shall be in English Bond. Half- brick walls including half brick skins of cavity walls shall be in stretcher bond. External faced brickwork shall commence two courses below finished ground level.

3. Completed brickwork shall be protected at all times from scaffold splash, mortar droppings and harmful effects of weather. Brickwork shall be allowed to set hard before cutting or chasing.

4. Bricks shall be wetted before they are laid. Partially completed work shall be wetted before laying further brickwork. The water used shall be no more than is sufficient to prevent absorption of moisture from the mortar.

5. Unless bricks are palleted only hand stacking and discharging of facing and engineering bricks shall be permitted whether at the place of manufacture, in transit, or at the site.

702. Work in Cold Weather

1. Bricks or blocks shall not be laid when the temperature in the shade is at, or below 3°C unless special precautions have been approved.

2. To prevent materials from becoming saturated or frozen they shall be protected by waterproof insulating covers.

3. Water and aggregates may be heated to ensure that the minimum temperature of the mortar when it is laid is not below 4°C. Mortar below 4°C shall not be used. Water should not however be heated above 60°C.

4. Precautions shall be taken to ensure that the mortar does not freeze before it has hardened. The finished work shall either be covered by an insulated waterproof covering or carried out and maintained in a heated enclosure as directed. The covering or heated enclosure shall not be removed without the permission of the Engineer and in any case not before three days have elapsed.

5. Clauses 702.2 and 702.4 shall apply also when the temperature is above 3°C but the Engineer deems that it may subsequently fall.

6. Antifreeze admixtures shall not be used.

703. Jointing and Pointing

1. Bricks and blocks shall be laid in mortar complying with Clause 338. They shall be laid on a full bed of mortar and all joints shall be filled.

2. Joints in external facing and external fair faced brickwork and blockwork shall be finished with a neat weather struck joint as the work proceeds.

3. Sample areas of walling shall be pointed and approved before pointing generally is commenced.

4. Internal fair faced brick and block walls shall be finished with neat flush joints effected by the use of a trowel or other approved method as the work proceeds.

74

5.   Where the surface of walling does not provide an adequate key the joints on faces of walls χ to be plastered or rendered shall be raked out 12 mm deep.

704. Damp Proof Course
1.   Damp proof courses shall comply with CP 102.

705. Cavity Walls
1.   Cavity walls shall be built with wall ties uniformly spaced at a maximum vertical and horizontal separation of 450 mm. Additional ties shall be provided within 225 mm of the sides of all openings so that there is one for each 300 mm of height of the opening.

2.   Ties within the cavity shall be kept free from mortar or mortar droppings. Any mortar or debris collecting at the bottom of the cavity wall shall be cleared out through temporary openings left for this purpose in the bottom courses.

3.   Wall cavities shall be filled with concrete Grade C7.5 to not less than 150 mm and not more than 300 mm below the damp proof course.

706. Plastering
1.   Concrete ceilings, ceiling beams and columns shall be prepared as necessary before plastering is commenced. Ridges left by shuttering imperfections shall be removed and the surface of in situ concrete shall be cleaned of all dust, loose particles and other matter. Surfaces of brickwork, hollow partitions, concrete and the like shall be thoroughly wetted immediately before plastering is commenced.

2.   Angles between walls and ceilings, vertical angles and joints between dissimilar backgrounds shall be reinforced with 90 mm wide scrim, set in plaster and trowelled flat.

3.   The thickness of 2 coat work, exclusive of keys shall be of the order of, but shall not exceed 12 mm. For 3 coat work the thickness shall be of the order of, but shall not normally exceed 18 mm. The thickness of 2 coat work applied to concrete ceilings and soffits, or plasterboard, shall not exceed 9 mm. The thickness of finishing coats shall be not less than 3 mm, well straightened, floated, trowelled and finished perfectly free from cracks and blisters. All batches shall be used as soon as possible after water has been added.

4.   When the air temperature is 5°C or less, the portion of the Works to be plastered shall be completely enclosed. The air temperature shall be raised to ensure that plastering is satisfactorily carried out and heat maintained until the completion of hydration.

707. Fixing of Plasterboard
1.   Plasterboard for ceilings shall be nailed to supports at 150 mm centres with 40 mm sherardised plasterboard nails. Joints shall be staggered. Noggins or other fixing surfaces shall be provided as necessary to ensure that edges of plasterboard are adequately secured. Ends of sheets shall be butted tightly and edges left with a gap not exceeding 5 mm.

2.   Where sheeting has been cut, nails shall be not less than 18 mm from cut edges. Nails shall be driven well home with heads slightly below the surface, but shall not break the paper.

3.   Angles between walls and ceilings, vertical angles and joints between boards shall be reinforced with 90 mm wide scrim applied with two coats of joint filling material.

708. Granolithic Concrete Floor Finishes
1.   Granolithic concrete floor finishes shall comply with Clause 438.

709. Floor Tiling
1. Floor tiling shall comply with CP 202.

710. Terrazzo
1. Terrazzo floor finishes shall comply with CP 204.

711. Wall Tiling
1. Wall tiling shall comply with BS 5385.

712. External Rendering
1. External rendering shall comply with BS 5262 and shall be applied to a total thickness of not less than 20 mm. The mix for both coats shall contain an approved waterproofing agent. The first coat shall be thrown on from a trowel, levelled with a straight edge, scratched and left to dry for not less than three days during which the daytime temperature reaches 15°C and not less than seven days otherwise or in wet weather. The suction of the first coat shall be adjusted as necessary by wetting before applying the second coat which shall be coloured as directed.

713. External Rendering 2 Coat Work with Stone or Pebble Dashed On
1. External walls shall be rendered 15 mm thick in 2 coats of 1:3 cement and sand mortar. Brickwork shall be thoroughly wetted and the joints raked out before the rendering coat is applied. The first coat shall be thrown on from a trowel, levelled with a straight edge and scratched for key. It shall be left to dry for not less than three days during which the daytime temperature reaches 15°C and not less than seven days otherwise or in wet weather. The suction of the first coat shall be adjusted as necessary by wetting. The stone or pebble dash shall be approved material free from sand and dust and passed through a 12 mm mesh screen. The stone or pebble dash shall be thrown on to, and pressed into the finishing coat while it is still soft, with sufficient force to bed each particle firmly. Each coat shall contain an approved waterproofing agent.

714. External Rendering 3 Coat Work with Stone or Pebble Incorporated in the Finishing Coat
1. The first coat shall comprise 1:4 cement and sand mortar and thrown on from a trowel, levelled with a straight edge and scratched. It shall be left to dry for not less than three days during which the daytime temperature reaches 15°C and not less than seven days otherwise or in wet weather before applying the second coat. The first coat shall be well wetted before applying the second coat of 1:4 cement and sand mortar. The second coat shall be allowed to dry similarly to the first. The third coat shall consist of one part coloured cement to 3 parts of a mixture of one part shingle or other approved material, graded 10 mm to 1.5 mm to 1 parts sand, gauged to a running consistency with approximately 16% of water and thrown on from a trowel. The total finished thickness shall be not less than 22 mm. Each coat shall contain an approved waterproofing agent.

715. Carpentry and Joinery, General
1. Timber to be incorporated in the work but excluding timber to be oiled or varnished shall, before delivery to Site, be pressure impregnated with a preservative to BS 5268 or BS 5589. The preservative shall be of a type suitable for use in conjunction with decorative paints. As far as possible, cutting and shaping of the timber shall be completed before preservative treatment is carried out. Where cutting or shaping has to be carried out after treatment, the surfaces so cut or worked shall be given 2 coats of the preservative. After treatment and before erection, timber shall be thoroughly dried out.

2. Workmanship shall comply with BS 1186. Except where work is *required by the Contract* to be to finished sizes, 3 mm shall be allowed for each wrot face. Frames, casings and other joinery fittings, except external door frames, shall be secured to fixing bricks or to hardwood fixing slips built in for the purpose. Where fixing bricks or slips have not been provided, walls shall be plugged with hardwood plugs or approved proprietary type plugs.

3.   Manufactured units to be painted shall be primed at the place of manufacture with an approved wood primer. The primer shall be applied by brush in an adequate and uniform coat to all surfaces including those to be bedded in.

716.   Timber Roofs
1.   Wall plates shall be halved and lapped at joints, and shall be securely fixed to walls.

2.   Rafters, collars, struts and braces shall be securely fixed to other roof members. Purlins, ridges, valleys and hips shall be in long lengths with the joints scarfed, wedged and bolted or jointed with approved connectors.

3.   Flats and gutters shall be covered with Type W.P.C. plywood or 25 mm tongued and grooved wrot boarding, firred to falls of not less than 1 in 120 for lead and copper and 1 in 60 for bitumen felt.

717.   Timber Floors
1.   Floor joists shall be either built into brickwork or blockwork or held in galvanised steel joist hangers and shall be trimmed as *required by the Contract*. Bridging shall be provided at not more than 1.8 m centres and shall be 50 mm thick to the full depth of the joists.

718.   Door Frames and Linings
1.   Posts to frames in block partitions shall be carried up, pinned to ceilings and diminished for plaster above the head of framing.

2.   External door frames shall be fixed to jambs with strong galvanised mild steel cramps, 3 to each jamb and of sufficient width to ensure secure fixing. They shall be secured at floor level by 75 mm x 20 mm dia. galvanised steel dowels let into the flooring and bedded in non-shrink epoxy grout.

719.   Windows
1.   Window frames shall be securely fixed to rebated openings in accordance with the manufacturer's instructions and shall be continuously pointed with gun applied butyl or other approved non-setting mastic.

720.   Glazing
1.   Glazing shall comply with BS 6262. Glass in metal sashes shall be well puttied front and back and secured with spring glazing clips. Glass in timber windows shall be well puttied front and back and secured with wire glazing pins. Glass in glazed doors shall be bedded in putty and fixed with glazing beads. Putty shall be full to sight lines of glazing bars and shall be neatly trimmed and cleaned off. Glazing shall be sound and watertight on completion. The putty shall be painted within a month of application.

721.   Painting
1.   Workmanship, surface preparation and application shall comply with BS 6150.

2.   Surfaces shall receive the number of applications stated in table 700A provided that the location of the works is in either the "mild" or "moderate" environmental categories as defined in Table 9 of BS 6150. All elements of the paint system, including the primer shall be compatible. Table 700A is intended for use in minor building works. Painting of steel structures shall comply with Series 900.

722.   Mastic Asphalt Roofing
1.   Mastic asphalt roofing shall comply with CP 144 and be laid on an underlay of sheathing felt, laid loose and with joints lapped at least 50 mm. The roof shall be finished with properly formed high points, water lines and mitred bays where required.

723. Bitumen Felt Roofing
1.   Built up bitumen felt roofing shall comply with CP 144.

724. Slating and Tiling
1.   Slating and tiling work shall comply with BS 5534.

2.   Laps, battens, fixings, beddings and underfelt for tiling shall comply with the manufacturer's recommendations.

725. Cladding
1.   Cladding shall comply with CP 143.

TABLE 700A

	Iron & Steel	Galvanised Steel	Copper & Brass	Aluminium	Softwood (External)	Softwood (Internal)	Untreated Hardwood (External)	Walls & Ceilings
Degreasing Solvent		1	1	1				
Red Lead Primer to BS 2523 or Red Lead/Red Oxide Primer	2							
Zinc Chromate Primer				1				
Calcium Plumbate Primer to BS 3698 Types A & B		1						
Primer for wood							1	
Primer for wood excluding water thinned primers					1			
Oil based or water thinned undercoat	1	1	1		1	1		1
Alkyd gloss or other finishing coat	1	1	1		2	1		1
Varnish, exterior grade full gloss							4	
Acrylic emulsion (thinned)								1
Acrylic emulsion								2

726. Concrete Roof Screeds
1. Concrete roof screeds shall be laid to a minimum thickness of 25 mm.

727. Plumbing
1. Plumbing for domestic water supply shall comply with BS 6700.

2. Plumbing for domestic above ground non-pressure sanitary pipework shall comply with BS 5572.

3. All plumbing work shall comply with the Water Byelaws.

728. Openings in Walls, Floors and Ceilings
1. The Contractor shall box out or cut openings through walls, floors and ceilings for the passage of pipes and cables and, where *required in the Contract*, shall provide and fix in position approved tube sleeves cut off flush with the finished surface. All openings and ducts shall be sealed on completion to prevent the passage of toxic or explosive gases.

729. Tolerances for Building Works
1. Tolerances for building works shall not exceed the permissible deviations given in BS 5606 for the corresponding types of work.

Fences, Markers and Indicator Posts

801. General Requirements for Temporary and Permanent Fences

1. All fences shall be regularly inspected and maintained.

2. Straining posts and struts shall be bedded in concrete and intermediate posts bedded as *required by the Contract*. Line wires shall not be strained until the concrete has hardened.

3. Concrete post and strut footings shall be Grade C7.5P concrete to Clause 419 and shall fill the hole for not less than half its depth and shall be well rammed as filling proceeds. After the concrete has hardened the remainder of the hole shall be filled with earth well rammed as filling proceeds.

802. Temporary Fencing

1. Where permanent fencing cannot be erected immediately, the Contractor shall erect and maintain temporary fencing. Access through the fencing shall be provided for owners, tenants and occupiers of adjacent lands as required.

2. Temporary fencing shall be of the following minimum standards as *required by the Contract*:-

   (a) Timber posts 75 mm by 75 mm, or equivalent round posts, at approximately 3 m intervals with 3 lines of 3.75 mm dia. wire at 450 mm, 750 mm and 1050 mm above the ground.

   (b) For fencing against animals, the top wire shall be barbed and where required sheep netting shall be 1050 mm high. Where netting is to be used, the middle line wire shall be omitted and the bottom wire placed 75 mm from the ground.

   (c) Electric fencing shall comply with BS 2632 and the IEE requirements.

   (d) Where a fence is required only to mark the boundary of the working area, it shall consist of a single line of 3.75 mm dia. wire adequately marked for visual purposes and properly strained at a height of 1050 mm above ground on timber posts as in (a) above.

3. Gaps formed in walls, hedges or fences shall be closed when required for the security of the affected areas and shall be stockproof where animals are kept in the adjoining land.

4. Fencing removed temporarily for the execution of the Works shall be reinstated as soon as possible, and adequate measures taken to ensure that there is no unauthorised entry to or escape of stock from adjoining land.

5. Fencing shall remain in position until it is replaced by permanent fencing or until completion of the relevant section of the Works.

803. Permanent Fencing

1. All permanent fencing shall comply with BS 1722.

2. Colouring of concrete fencing posts shall be by the addition of an approved pigment during manufacture.

804. Gates and Gate Posts

1. Single and double domestic gates shall comply with BS 4092. Gate posts shall comply with BS 3470 and shall be bedded as detailed in Clause 801.3.

2. Field gates and posts shall comply with BS 3470 and shall be of a height to match the adjoining fence. Gate posts shall be bedded in concrete which shall be well rammed as filling proceeds, brought to ground surface and sloped upwards towards the post. Gate posts shall butt against the adjacent straining post or other boundary. Where a gate post is to be against a straining post both shall be erected at the same time.

3.   Steel gates shall be constructed of tubes complying with BS 6323 with exposed ends of tubes capped and sealed, or of sections complying with BS 4360. Welding shall comply with BS 5135. Gates and fittings galvanised after manufacture shall comply with BS 729: Part 1 and shall have a coating of at least 600g of zinc per m^2 of surface area or a thickness of 85 microns. Steel gates to be painted shall be delivered to site with one works coat of an approved non-toxic primer.

4.   Steel gates in chain link or mesh fencing shall have rectangular frames with all corners mitred, saddled or gusseted. The hanging and shutting stiles shall extend vertically upwards 450 mm to carry three lines of barbed wire. Where required intermediate vertical extension arms 450 mm long of tube or section to suit the gate, shall be welded to the top of the frame and drilled or slotted to support the barbed wire. Infilling of each gate frame shall be a purpose made panel matching the fence and edged with stretcher bars bolted securely to the framework. The outside face of each gate shall be flush with the fence.

805. Removal and Re-erection of Fences and Gates

1.   Fences, gates and posts which are to be re-erected shall have existing paint removed and be primed and painted with three coats of oil paint as specified in Clause 806 or where appropriate be re-creosoted with two coats of creosote complying with BS 144. Gates and posts shall be re-erected in compliance with Clause 804.

806. Pretreatment and Painting of Fences, Gates and Posts

1.   Pretreatment and painting shall be carried out in accordance with Clauses 916 and 917. Where the work is normally accessible to livestock only non-toxic materials shall be used.

807. Marker and Indicator Posts

1.   Posts shall be bedded in concrete in accordance with Clause 801.3.

2.   Marker and indicator posts shall be vibrated precast reinforced concrete to the dimensions and patterns as *required by the Contract*.

808. Marker Buoys

1.   Marker buoys shall comply with the regulations of the Department of Transport Marine Directorate.

Metal Structures, Cladding and Painting

901. Metal Structures, General

1. Structural metalwork shall comply with:-
   (a)   BS 449 or BS 5950 for structural steelwork,
   (b)   BS CP 118 for structural aluminium,
   (c)   BS 2853 for overhead runway beams.

902. Drawings

1. Where *required by the Contract*, the Contractor shall submit for written approval copies in duplicate of:-
   (a)   working drawings of the structure, including details of connections and joints,
   (b)   drawings and details of temporary bracing, and
   (c)   drawings for setting out the structure foundations.

2. No fabrication shall commence until the working drawings have been approved in writing.

903. Fabrication

1. Fabricated structural steelwork shall be within the tolerances specified in BS 5950. Tolerances for fabricated structural aluminium shall be as for steelwork or as *required by the Contract*. All plates and sections shall be true to form and free from twists and shall be accurately straightened, planed, shaped or extruded as necessary, without defacing or weakening the material.

2. At all stages of fabrication, structural members shall be positively identified in accordance with an approved marking scheme. For the purposes of marking for erection, every part shall be marked with an approved durable and distinguishing mark in such a way as not to damage the material.

3. Due account shall be taken of the effects of temperature, particularly on aluminium, in measuring, marking out and fabrication.

4. The ends of all sections shall be accurately sawn unless otherwise approved.

5. Light angle sections may be cut by shearing or cropping provided that the ends are dressed flush and all burrs removed.

6. Machine flame cutting of steelwork may be approved. Hand flame cutting will be considered only where it is impracticable to use machine flame cutting and, provided that properly prepared templates and guides are used. Flame cutting shall not be used for aluminium.

7. Cut edges shall be true to profile and free from notches and cutting serrations. Ends shall be dressed flush, with all burrs removed.

8. Holes for fasteners or pins shall be drilled unless otherwise approved. Burrs shall be removed from holes before assembly. Holes and contact surfaces for high strength friction grip connections shall comply with BS 4604.

9. All matching holes for fasteners or pins shall register with each other so that fasteners can be inserted freely through the assembled members in a direction at right angles to the faces in contact.

10. In structural steelwork, for bolts not exceeding 24 mm dia., holes shall not be more than 2 mm greater in diameter than the bolt, and for bolts over 24 mm dia., holes shall not be more than 3 mm greater than the diameter of the bolt, or as *required by the Contract*. In structural aluminium, holes shall be sized in accordance with CP 118 or as *required by the Contract*. Holes for close fitting bolts shall be reamed to exact size after the component parts have been clamped together for assembly.

11.   Care shall be taken over the aesthetic appearance of structural metalwork which is to remain exposed.

904. Assembly

1.   All components shall be assembled in such a manner as to prevent bending, twisting or otherwise damaging the members. Assembly tolerances for structural steelwork shall comply with BS 5950. Assembly tolerances for structural aluminium shall be as for steelwork or as *required by the Contract*.

2.   Drifting to align holes shall not enlarge the holes or distort the metal.

3.   Welding of structural steelwork shall comply with BS 5135. Welding of structural aluminium shall comply with CP 118.

4.   Bolts shall have a washer fitted under the nut and the length of the bolt shall be such that at least one clear thread shows above the nut after tightening. The length of unthreaded shank of the bolt shall be not more than the sum of the thicknesses of the individual component parts to be bolted together less three times the thread pitch. For structural aluminium, washers shall also be used under all bolt heads. Tapered washers shall be used under all bolt heads and nuts bearing on bevelled surfaces. Nuts shall be properly, but not excessively, tightened.

5.   Bolts subject to vibration shall be provided with lock nuts or other approved devices as *required by the Contract*.

6.   Where slotted holes are provided for movement connections as *required by the Contract*, the joint shall be free to move.

7.   Preliminary and protective treatment of structural steelwork shall comply with BS 5950 and shall be as *required by the Contract*. Preliminary and protective treatment of structural aluminium shall comply with CP 118 and shall be as *required by the Contract*.

8.   Trial assembly shall be undertaken at the fabricator's workshop to prove the accuracy of the workmanship prior to delivery to Site.

905. Delivery, Handling and Erection

1.   Fabricated parts shall be handled and stacked in such a way that damage is not caused to the components and metalwork shall be stored in clean conditions. Means shall be provided to minimise damage to protective treatment. Where appearance is important, aluminium shall be stored in dry conditions, clear of the ground and out of contact with other metals and materials such as cement and damp timber. Surfaces of aluminium for architectural use shall be protected with strippable tapes, waxes or lacquers while danger of damage exists.

2.   All metalwork shall be protected from damage in transit. Particular care shall be taken to stiffen free ends, prevent permanent distortion and protect all machined surfaces. Aluminium shall be packed to avoid abrasion and, where appearance is important, surface corrosion and staining.

3.   All bolts, nuts, washers, screws, small plates and articles shall be suitably packed, identified and stored.

4.   The erection of the structural metalwork shall be planned and carried out by the Contractor so as to ensure safe working conditions at all times. Where *required by the Contract*, details of erection systems and temporary bracing, including calculations, designs and working methods shall be submitted to the Engineer for written approval.

5.   Metalwork shall be securely bolted or fastened to ensure that it can withstand all loadings liable to be encountered during erection of the structure, including those from erection plant and its operation. Any temporary bracing or restraint shall be left in position until erection is sufficiently advanced to allow its safe removal.

6.   All connections for temporary bracing, bolts, members and the like provided for erection purposes, shall be made so that they do not weaken the permanent structure or impair serviceability.

7.   Permanent connections shall not be made until a sufficient amount of the structure has been aligned, levelled, plumbed and temporarily connected to ensure that members will not be displaced during subsequent erection or alignment of the remainder of the structure. No operation shall be carried out which would damage, overstress or disfigure any part of the structural metalwork.

8.   Damage to any part of the structural metalwork, either before or during erection, shall be brought to the notice of the Engineer who may direct that the damaged part shall be replaced. All repair work must be approved in writing.

9.   The Contractor shall ensure the correct positioning and levelling of the structure in relation to the approved datums. The accuracy with which metalwork is assembled and erected shall be in accordance with Clause 907.

10.   Due account shall be taken of the effects of temperature on the structure and measuring instruments when measurements are made for setting out and erection, and for dimensional checks carried out subsequently.

11.   Any damage to the protective treatment of metalwork shall be made good as approved in writing.

906.   Supports and Foundations

1.   Foundation bolts shall be set out within the limits for position and level specified in Clause 907.

2.   Foundation bolts shall be held firmly in position during all setting-in operations and care shall be taken to ensure that the full movement tolerances are achieved.

3.   Bolts, threads and nuts shall be protected against damage or corrosion and kept clean at all stages of construction.

4.   Tubes to be concreted into foundations as bolt pockets shall be securely fixed and effectively sealed to prevent ingress of grout during placing of the surrounding concrete.

5.   Pockets formed around foundation bolts shall be kept clean and free from water.

6.   Packings, shims and other supporting devices shall be flat, of adequate strength and rigidity, and not larger than necessary. Where packings are to be left in position and subsequently grouted they shall be placed so that they are totally enclosed by the grout.

7.   Cement based grouts used for bedding bases or bearing plates on concrete foundations shall be one of the following: −
   (a)   Neat Portland cement of a thickness not exceeding 25 mm. The grout shall be mixed as thickly as possible consistent with fluidity and shall be poured under a suitable head so that the space is completely filled.

   (b)   Fluid Portland cement mortar of a thickness between 25 mm and 50 mm. The mortar shall be not leaner than 1:1 cement to fine aggregate and shall be mixed as thickly as possible consistent with fluidity. The mortar shall then be poured under a suitable head and tamped until the space has been completely filled.

   (c)   Dry as possible Portland cement mortar of thickness not less than 50 mm. The mortar shall be not leaner than 1:2 cement to fine aggregate and shall be consolidated by thoroughly ramming with a suitable blunt rammer against properly fixed supports until the space has been completely filled.

8. Where *required by the Contract*, the following special grouts may be used:-
   (a)   mortar or fine concrete containing suitable admixtures, including the use of expanding additives to avoid shrinkage, or

   (b)   expanding grout, or

   (c)   resin-based grout.

9. No grouting shall be carried out until a sufficient portion of the structure has been aligned, levelled, plumbed and adequately braced by other structural components which have been levelled and are securely held by their permanent connections. Immediately before grouting, the spaces shall be clear of all debris and free water.

10. Stanchions in pocket bases shall be grouted with fine dense Portland cement concrete having a characteristic cube strength at 28 days not less than that of the surrounding concrete base nor less than 20 N/mm^2, and with a maximum aggregate size of 10 mm. The pocket shall be filled initially with concrete up to a height of at least two thirds of the embedded length of the stanchion and shall then remain undisturbed for at least 48 hours.

11. All metalwork in foundations shall be solidly encased in consolidated Portland cement concrete having a characteristic cube strength of not less than 20 N/mm^2 at 28 days . A minimum cover of 100 mm shall be provided to any metalwork where the concrete surrounding it is adjacent to the soil.

907. Erection Tolerances

1. Unless otherwise *required by the Contract*, the following erection tolerances shall apply:-
   (a)   Connection to concrete elements

      (i)   The position of the centre of any bolt at the point where it connects to the metalwork shall not vary by more than ± 3 mm from its specified position for bolts rigidly cast in, and ± 5 mm for bolts in sleeves. The position of the other end of the bolt shall be set such that any resulting slope of the bolt is not so large as to cause difficulties in fitting the connection to the structural frame.

      (ii)   The projection of the end of the bolt shall not deviate from that specified by more than + 25 mm or -5 mm.

      (iii) For bolts in sleeves, it shall be possible to move the bolt to the full extent of the sleeve as provided.

   (b)   Column bases

      (i)   The position in plan of a column at the base shall not deviate from the specified position by more than 10 mm along either of the principal setting out axes.

      (ii)   The level of the underside of a base plate shall not deviate from the specified level by more than ± 10 mm.

   (c)   Plumbing and alignment of columns

      (i)   The deviation of the top of a column from its specified position relative to the base shall not exceed the greater of 5 mm or 1/600 of the height, base to cap, in any direction, except in the case of the deviation of the tops of the columns of a portal frame measured in the plane of the frame.

   (d)   Position in plan of members

      (i)   Members other than columns shall not deviate from their specified position relative to the columns to which they are connected by more than 5 mm.

   (e)   Levels

      (i)   The level of the top of the metalwork shall be within ± 10 mm of the specified level, and shall not vary by more than ± 5 mm within any distance of 5 m.

908. Cladding, General
1. Unless otherwise *required by the Contract*, cladding shall comply with CP 143 for sheet roof and wall coverings.

2. Roof and wall cladding shall be as *required by the Contract* and details of the system proposed, including all weatherings, fixings and accessories, shall be approved in writing.

3. The cladding system shall be completely windproof and weathertight.

909. Fixing of Cladding
1. External sheeting shall be fixed, as *required by the Contract*, either by:-
   (a)   direct connection to the purlins, or

   (b)   connection through the crest of the profile to timber battens which have been prefixed to the purlins along with inner sheeting.

2. All side laps shall be properly fixed together to prevent any independent deflection and movement between the sheets. End laps shall be kept to a minimum by the use of as long a sheet length as possible and, where they do occur they shall be at supports and have an overlap of 150 mm.

3. All end and side laps shall be sealed with approved gun grade mastic applied between the sheets along the lines of the fasteners at the laps.

4. All flashings and the like and profile fillers fitted at eaves, gutters and soffits shall be securely fixed to prevent the ingress of wind and weather.

910. Accessories to Cladding
1. Panels shall be fixed with colour matched fasteners in accordance with the manufacturer's instructions. Roof exits for pipes, ventilators and the like shall be trimmed using all necessary sleeves, flashing and sealants.

2. All verges, ridges, soffits, internal and external corners, closure plates around openings and the like shall be in a material appropriate to the roofing and cladding, colour matched and fixed in accordance with the manufacturer's instructions. Gutters shall be of a type and material as *required by the Contract*.

911. Painting, General Requirements for Surface Preparation
1. Surfaces to receive paint shall have all contaminants such as millscale, rust, oil, grease, dirt and loosely adhering old paint removed prior to paint application. The surface preparation shall be in accordance with Table 900A and shall be suitable for the selected paint system.

2. Areas affected by surface contaminants shall be cleaned down using a liquid cleaner and water before any painterwork is commenced. Cleaning agents shall be approved and only cold clean water shall be used for washing down.

3. The type capacity and condition of all surface preparatory equipment including tools, abrasive wheels, discs and grinding wheels shall be approved. The edges of existing coatings adjacent to abraded or blast cleaned areas shall be bevelled back where practicable into sound and firmly adhering material.

4. Immediately prior to painting, the Contractor shall ensure that the surfaces are:-

   (a)   prepared to the specified standard,
   (b)   free from all detrimental contamination,

    (c)   free from dust and grit, and

    (d)   dry and ready for painting.

912. Cleaning and Washing Down
1. Cleaning down shall be carried out by one of the following methods:-
    (a)   Dry cleaning by scrubbing with a dry stiff bristle brush.

    (b)   Wet cleaning by scrubbing with a stiff bristle brush using water and an approved liquid detergent.

2. Immediately after cleaning down, all surfaces shall be washed and rinsed with clean fresh water and allowed to dry thoroughly before any paint is applied.

913. Abrading Aided by Scraping and Wire Brushing
1. Any encrusted rust, foreign matter or paint which may be difficult to remove by abrading alone shall be dislodged by scraping, aided by hand or power wire brushing as necessary or other approved method. This work shall be completed before abrading commences.

2. Abrading shall be carried out using one or more of the following methods:-
    (a)   Abrasive paper or other material.
    (b)   Flexible abrasive disc mounted on a power driven flexible pad.
    (c)   A power drive arbor or spindle mounted flexible abrasive flap wheel.
Abrading tools may be used to remove weld splatter. If approved wet abrading may be employed for preparation over sound undercoats.

3. A burnished appearance caused by the polishing in of old paint, rust or dirt will not be accepted.

4. Areas of corroded steel or unsound paint coverings prepared by abrading down to bare or bright steel shall be protected by a surface tolerant rust inhibiting primer before cleaning down or other preparation of adjacent surfaces.

914. Blast Cleaning
1. Blast cleaning shall be carried out by one of the following methods:-
    (a)   Dry blast cleaning using dry air and abrasive.
    (b)   Wet blast cleaning using low pressure air, water and abrasive. The air and water pressure at the nozzle shall not exceed $14.0\,Kgf/cm^2$ and shall be fully adjustable below this level. The system shall incorporate a mechanical metering device, remotely controlled from the nozzle, to enable the operator to regulate from zero to maximum the quantity of abrasive being fed into the air and water mixture. During abrasive cleaning the air, water and abrasive shall be thoroughly mixed and projected onto the surface to be cleaned through a single bore nozzle.
    (c)   Wet blast cleaning using high pressure air, water and abrasive. The water pressure shall not exceed $562\,Kgf/cm^2$. The system shall incorporate a mechnical metering device controlled at the nozzle, to enable the operator to regulate from zero to maximum the quantity of abrasive being fed into the water.
    (d)   Combined wet and dry blast cleaning. Wet blast cleaning using low pressure air, water and abrasive in accordance with Paragraph (b) shall be followed after an approved interval by dry blast cleaning in accordance with Paragraph (a) of all the previously wet blast cleaned area.

2. Unless otherwise *required by the Contract* wet cleaning down and abrading shall be carried out before dry blast cleaning on adjacent surfaces.
Finally prepared metal surfaces shall be protected within a period as specified in Clause 919.5 or as *required by the Contract* with a surface tolerant rust inhibiting priming coat including any appropriate stripe coat.

915. Grinding

1. Grinding wheels and discs shall be of the size, shape and grade of coarseness appropriate to the particular operation.

2. The speed of revolution shall be that recommended by the manufacturer.

3. Unless otherwise *required by the Contract* grinding shall be carried out after surface preparation by other methods, including cleaning down, has been completed.

4. Surfaces prepared by grinding to bright steel shall be protected by a surface tolerant rust inhibiting primer before cleaning down or other preparation of adjacent surfaces.

916. Standards of Prepared Surfaces

1. Prepared surface shall be free of:-
   (a)   visible gloss on sound paint to provide a satisfactory key for the primer,

   (b)   unsound paint,

   (c)   if *required by the Contract* all paint, and

   (d)   contamination detrimental to existing or subsequent coatings.

2. 'Sound paint' means paint which is sound down to a metal substrate.

3. 'Unsound paint' means paint showing signs of disruption, rusting through or inadequate adhesion, or which is covering a metal substrate where there is rust scale, loose rust, loose mill scale or other detrimental corrosion product.

4. Exposed steel substrate shall be prepared as *required by the Contract* to one of the following standards:-
   (a)   'Clean steel' by blast cleaning, to 2nd quality as in BS 4232.

   (b)   'Bare steel' by blast cleaning or abrading, removal of all rust scale, loose rust and loose mill scale.

   (c)   'Bare steel' by abrading, removal of all rust scale, loose rust and loose mill scale.

   (d)   'Bright steel' by abrading, removal of all surface rust and mill scale to produce an overall generally bright appearance.

   (e)   'Bright steel' by grinding, removal of all welding splatter and other surface defects leaving an overall generally bright appearance. Rounding of sharp edges shall be to a radius of approximately 1 mm.

917. Paint

1. Paint systems shall be as approved and shall be selected as *required by the Contract* from Table 900 or when for use in a marine environment.

2. Paint shall comply with Clause 340.

3. Paints forming any one paint system shall be obtained from a single manufacturer and, unless otherwise approved, the source of supply shall not change during the course of the contract.

4. Paint shall be delivered in sealed tins with the contents clearly indicated.

5. Paint will be suitable in all respects for the purposes intended, and for satisfactory application at the recommended minimum thicknesses and by the specified methods.

6. Where painted surfaces are accessible to farm animals, lead free paints shall be used.

Table 900A Treatment and painting of new or previously painted metalwork

	SURFACE CONDITION	SURFACE PREPARATION	TREATMENT	PAINT SYSTEM (SEE TABLE 900.B)
1.	Sound paint with slight deterioration but no rusting	Dry bristle brush, clean and wash down	Primer, undercoat and finish	A, C or E
2.	Sound paint exhibiting chalking or exposure of previous finish	Wire brush, clean and wash down	Primer, undercoat and finish	A, C or E
3.	Thin paint exhibiting blistering or pinhead rusting	Abrade, scrape and wire brush, clean and wash down	Patch prime any bare metal and follow with primer, undercoat and finish	B, D or E
4.	Thin paint, flaking in parts with rusted areas less than 25% of total	Thin or flaking paint : abrade, scrape and wire brush, clean and wash down Rusted areas: remove rust by abrading methods, clean and wash down	Patch prime any bare metal and follow with primer, undercoat and finish	A with B or C with D or E
5.	Bare metal or thin paint, flaking in parts with rusted areas greater than 25% of total	Remove all coating, rust or millscale, clean and wash down	Patch prime where necessary and build up new system with primer, undercoat and finish	B or D

918. Storage of Paint

1.   On delivery to site paint shall be unloaded directly into a lockfast paint store. The temperature of the store shall be kept within 4°C and 27°C. Paint which reaches temperatures outwith this range shall be discarded.

2.   Paint which has not been used within the 'shelf life' recommended by the manufacturer shall be discarded.

919. Application of Paint

1.   Paint shall be suitable for the conditions at site, including temperature and humidity, and able to be applied satisfactorily in these conditions.

2.   Paint shall not be applied under the following conditions:-
   (a)   When the ambient temperature falls below 4°C or the relative humidity rises above 90 per cent, or

   (b)   during rain, snow, fog, mist or in a dust laden atmosphere, or

   (c)   when the amount of moisture on the surface to be painted, or that likely to accumulate thereon may have a harmful effect on the paint, or

   (d)   when wind borne dust may have a harmful effect on the paint.

3.   Each coat of paint of a specified system shall be generally free from surface defects including runs, bare patches, thickening or sagging as defined in BS 2015. The finished system shall have an even and uniform appearance, due allowance being made for the change in film thickness at the edges of patch coats.

4.   Exposure times for prepared steel shall be as follows:-
   (a)   Clean steel prepared by dry blast cleaning or bright steel prepared by abrading or grinding shall be primed within 4 hours.

   (b)   Clean steel prepared by wet blast cleaning only, shall be primed within 4 hours of being dry enough for painting.

   (c)   Clean steel prepared by combined wet and dry blast cleaning shall be primed within 4 hours of dry blast cleaning.

   (d)   Bare steel prepared by dry blast cleaning or abrading shall be overcoated within 48 hours.

   (e)   Bare steel prepared by wet blast cleaning shall be primed within 24 hours of being dry enough for painting.

   (f)   Bare steel prepared by wet and dry blast cleaning shall be primed within 48 hours of dry blast cleaning.

5.   Paint overcoating times shall be as follows:-
   (a)   Primers on steel shall be overcoated within 7 days and the next coat applied within 14 days.

   (b)   Surfaces of existing paint coats which have been prepared to sound paint, cleaned down only or abraded only to remove gloss shall be overcoated within 7 days.

6.   Paint shall be applied by one of the following methods:-
   (a)   Brush.

   (b)   Airless spray.

   (c)   Air pressure spray

7.   All coats in a paint system including any stripe coat shall be in contrasting colours to aid identification.

94

Table 900B Paint systems for painting of new or previously painted metalwork

System	Coat	Description
SYSTEM A * (mdft 130 μm)	PRIMER:	Alkyd or epoxy ester based primer to BS 5493 : 1977, Table 4F, Part 2, FP3 or FP4, mdft 30 μm.
	UNDERCOAT:	Alkyd or epoxy ester based undercoat to BS 5493 : 1977, Table 4F, Part 3 FU2 or FR4, mdft 50 μm.
	FINISH:	Alkyd or epoxy ester based finish to BS 5493 : 1977, Table 4, Part 4, FF3 or FF4, mdft 50 μm.
SYSTEM B (mdft 200 μm)	PATCH PRIMER:	Two component surface tolerant rust inhibiting primer, mdft 50 μm.
	PRIMER:	Two component surface tolerant rust inhibiting primer, mdft 100 μm.
	UNDERCOAT:	Alkyd or epoxy ester based undercoat to BS 5493 : 1977, Table 4F, Part 3 FU2 or FR4, mdft 50 μm.
	FINISH:	Alkyd or epoxy ester based finish to BS 5493 : 1977, Table 4, Part 4, FF3 or FF4, mdft 50 μm.
SYSTEM C (mdft 200 μm)	PRIMER:	Two component surface tolerant rust inhibiting primer, mdft 100 μm.
	UNDERCOAT:	One component chemical-resistant undercoat to BS 5493 : 1977, Table 4H, Part 3 HU1 mdft 50 μm.
	FINISH:	One component chemical-resistant finish to BS 5493 : 1977, Table 4H, Part 4, HF1, mdft 50 μm.
SYSTEM D (mdft 200 μm)	PATCH PRIMER:	Two component surface tolerant rust inhibiting primer, mdft 50 μm.
	PRIMER:	Two component surface tolerant rust inhibiting primer, mdft 100 μm.
	UNDERCOAT:	One component chemical-resistant undercoat to BS 5493 : 1977, Table 4H, Part 3 HU1 mdft 50 μm.
	FINISH:	One component chemical-resistant finish to BS 5493 : 1977, Table 4H, Part 4, HF1, mdft 50 μm.
SYSTEM E for existing bitumen coated surfaces (mdft 300 μm)	PATCH PRIMER :	Black bitumen coating primer to BS 3416, Typ I, Class A, mdft 50 μm.
	UNDERCOAT:	Black bitumen coating solution to BS 3416, Type I, Class A, mdft 200 μm.
	FINISH:	Black bitumen coating solution to BS 3416, Type I, Class A, mdft 100 μm.

* (mdft 130 μm) - minimum depth of finished thickness 130 microns (dry)

95

8. Stripe coat shall be applied at welds, brackets, connections, fasteners including washers, and external corners.

9. In areas prepared down to steel substrate stripe coat shall be applied over the primer. In areas prepared down to sound paint, a stripe coat shall be applied before the primer.

10. Only thinners recommended by the manufacturers of the paint shall be used and only in the recommended proportions.

11. Wet film thickness gauges shall be used where practicable to check that the wet film thickness for each coat is not less than

$$\frac{\text{minimum dry film thickness} \times 100}{\text{percentage volume of solids}}$$

The Contractor shall ensure that the progressive total thickness of the applied coats will achieve the specified minimum total dry film thickness for the system, without exceeding the maximum permissible thickness of any of the coats as recommended by the manufacturer.
The dry film thickness of a paint system and its constituent parts shall not be less than the minimum finished thickness specified in Table 900.B.

920. Protection of Adjoining Areas
1. The Contractor shall by the use of screens, shields or other means protect watercourses, traffic, pedestrians and adjoining properties from nuisance, disturbance, pollution and interference.

921. Procedure Trials
1. At the start of the Works the Contractor shall carry out surface preparation procedure trials on areas totalling between 2 m^2 and 10 m^2 as designated by the Engineer, employing the labour and equipment to be used in the Works. The remaining surface preparation shall not be started until the results of these trials and the painting procedure trials specified in Clause 921.2 below have been approved.

2. Immediately following the satisfactory completion of the surface preparation trials the Contractor shall carry out painting procedure trials on the prepared surfaces, employing the labour and equipment to be used in the Works.

3. Any adjustment to the paint formulations shown to be required by the trials shall be approved and the adjustments shall be made at the paint manufacturer's works.

4. Before the Contractor employs new operators or equipment he shall carry out further procedure trials unless otherwise approved.

Biological Filters and Sludge Drying Beds

1001. General

1.   The Contractor shall provide and subsequently remove facilities for storing reasonable quantities of filter media adjacent to the biological filters and drying beds. The surface of the storage areas shall be such that it will prevent contamination of the filter media by soil or other impurities. Filter media shall not be tipped directly into a biological filter or sludge drying bed but shall be deposited in the storage areas only.

2.   Following deposition in the storage area, filter media shall subsequently be removed and handled by approved means only. Media shall not be handled by grabs or other mechanical loading equipment.

3.   Prior to being placed in the filter bed the media shall be thoroughly washed or passed over an approved vibrating screen to remove fine particles of dust. Notwithstanding the tolerance limits specified in BS   1438 the quantity of grit and dust particles finer than 5 mm in the media as placed in the filter bed shall not exceed 1% by weight.

4.   Transportation of the filter media to the final position shall be by belt conveyors or hand barrows, loaded directly from the washing or screening area by approved clinker forks only. Precautions shall be taken to prevent damage to or displacement of filter tiles and on no occasion after final washing or screening shall filter media be allowed to fall freely from a height exceeding 1 m. Mechanically propelled vehicles shall not be permitted to traverse or stand upon the placed media or filter tiles. Hand barrows shall be restricted to adequate timbered runways. Facilities shall be provided for workmen to clean their footwear and hand barrows before entering the filter media.

1002. Biological Filters

1.   Filter media for biological filters shall be placed in two layers varying in depth to suit the fall in the floor. The top layer shall conform to Clause 321.2(a). The bottom layer shall conform to Clause 320.2(b). The depth of the bottom layer shall be 150 mm over the top of the filter tiles. All filter media shall be hand placed around pipework and ventilation shafts.

2.   Concrete bases for duck foot bends shall be made true and level to ensure accurate alignment and levelling of the distributor arms.

1003. Sludge Drying Beds without Full Tile Coverage

1.   Filter media shall be placed in three layers. The bottom layer shall vary in depth to suit the fall in the invert and shall conform to Clause 321.3(a)(i). The middle layer shall be 75 mm deep and shall conform to Clause 320.3(a)(ii). The top layer shall be 75 mm deep and shall conform to Clause 320.3(a)(iii).

1004. Sludge Drying Beds with Full Tile Coverage

1.   Filter media shall be placed in one layer varying in depth to suit the fall in the invert and shall conform to Clause 321.3(b).

1005. Surface Dressing Material for Sludge Drying Beds

1.   A layer of surface dressing material 50 mm deep shall be placed on top of the filter media of sludge drying beds. The material shall be sand conforming to Clause 321.3(c), ash conforming to Clause 320.3(d) or other material as *required by the Contract*.

Roads, Hardstandings and Footways

1101. Preparation, Surface Treatment and Use of Formation

1.   Preparation and surface treatment of the formation shall be carried out only after the completion of sub-grade drainage, services or ducts within the formation. Trenches for sub-grade drainage, services and ducts shall be reinstated in accordance with Clause 209 immediately prior to laying the sub-base or roadbase where no sub-base is required. The sequence of operations shall be as follows:-

(a)   Formations of soft materials

(i)   The surface of the formation shall, after reinstatement of any soft areas, be well cleaned and made free of mud and slurry.

(ii)   The surface shall be compacted by 4 passes of a smooth wheeled roller having a mass per metre width of roll of 4,400 to 6,000 kg.

(iii)   The formation shall be regulated and trimmed in accordance with Clause 1102.

(iv)   The trimmed formation shall be rolled by 1 pass of a smooth wheeled roller having a mass per metre width of roll not less than 2,100 kg.

(v)   Areas of completed formation shall be limited to suit the rate of deposition of sub-base. Formations of cohesive material shall not remain exposed to rain which may cause degradation, and shall be not be left uncovered overnight.

(b)   Formations of rock fill
The formation shall be blinded with approved fine material and completed in accordance with (a) (iii) and (iv).

(c)   Formations of rock cuttings
Surface irregularities under formation shall be regulated in accordance with Clause 1102 with clean hard broken stone or Grade C7.5 concrete.

2.   Construction plant and vehicular traffic other than that required for preparation of the formation shall not be operated on the formation unless approved protection of the surface is provided.

1102. Horizontal Alignments and Surface Levels of Pavement Courses

1.   Horizontal alignments shall be determined from one edge of the pavement surface as *required by the Contract*. The edge of the pavement and all other parallel alignments shall be correct within a tolerance of ±25 mm except for kerbs, channel blocks and edge lines which shall be laid with a smooth alignment within a tolerance of ±13 mm.

2.   The levels of pavement courses and formation shall be determined from the true final pavement surface. The vertical depth below the true final pavement surface of any point on the surface of the formation or intermediate courses shall be within the following tolerances:-

Formation	+ 20 mm
	− 30 mm
Sub-base	+ 10 mm
	− 30 mm
Roadbase	± 15 mm
Basecourse	± 6 mm
Road surface	± 6mm

3.   The combination of the above tolerances shall not result in a reduction in the thickness of the pavement, excluding the sub-base, by more than 15 mm from the specified thickness, or the bituminous wearing course by more than 5 mm from that specified.

4.   The final pavement and basecourse surfaces shall be tested with a 3 m straight edge parallel to the centre line of the road and shall have no greater depression under the straight edge than 3 mm and 6 mm respectively.

5.   Where any tolerance is exceeded the defective surface shall be rectified in the following manner:-

    (a)   Formation level
          If the surface is too high it shall be trimmed and recompacted in accordance with Clause 1101. If the surface is too low additional fresh suitable material shall be laid and compacted in accordance with Clause 1101.

    (b)   Roadbases and sub-bases
          The top 75 mm of the defective area shall be scarified, reshaped with added material as necessary, and recompacted in accordance with Clause 1105.

    (c)   Basecourse and wearing courses
          These shall have level or tolerance measurements made while the material is still warm and rectification, where necessary, carried out immediately. Otherwise the full depth of the layer shall be removed over the defective area and replaced with fresh material in accordance with Clauses 1105 and 1106.

    (d)   Concrete slabs
          Testing of the concrete surface for compliance with tolerances shall be carried out after sweeping, not less than 36 hours or more than 35 days after placing the concrete. High areas shall be ground down by approved means and low areas rectified by cutting out the surface to a depth of not less than 25 mm and replacing with concrete to an approved mix design and method of replacement, both surfaces being textured to match adjacent finishes.

1103.   Cold Weather Working

1.   Road pavement material in a frozen condition shall not be incorporated in the Works.

2.   Road pavement materials shall not be laid on any surface which is frozen or covered with ice.

3.   Materials containing tar or bitumen binders shall not be laid if the temperature of the surface to be covered is at or below 2°C. Where the surface is dry, unfrozen and free of ice, laying may proceed at air temperatures in the shade at or above -1°C on a rising thermometer.

4.   The temperature of concrete or cement bound material in any pavement layer shall not be less than 5°C at the point of delivery. These materials shall not be laid when the air temperature in the shade falls below 3°C.

5.   During the first 20 days after placing sections of concrete pavement or the first 7 days in the case of other cement bound materials, the period which would otherwise be required before running any traffic on them shall be increased by 1 day for each night on which the temperature of the surface of the layer in question falls to 0°C or below.

1104.   Use of Surfaces by Construction Traffic

1.   Construction plant used on pavements under construction shall not cause damage to the sub-grade or the pavement courses already completed.

2.   The wheels or tracks of plant moving over the various pavement courses shall be kept free of deleterious material.

3.   Where construction traffic is to use the sub-base it shall be improved where necessary to avoid damage to the sub-base, any capping and the sub-grade. Any permanent thickening shall be across the whole width of the pavement. Temporary thickening shall not impede drainage of the sub-base or the sub-grade.

4.   Wheels or tracks of concreting plant shall not use any part of a newly constructed pavement within 10 days of laying.

5.   Vehicular traffic shall not be run on a concrete pavement within a period of 14 days from its completion during the months of June to August inclusive or 20 days at other times. Vehicles shall not run on the pavement until the joints are permanently or temporarily sealed.

6.   Bituminous material shall be kept clean and uncontaminated while not covered by succeeding layers or surface treatment. Only traffic engaged in the construction of pavement courses shall be permitted access to bituminous materials. Any contamination shall be made good by cleaning or by removing the layer and replacing it in accordance with Clause 1106.

1105.   Sub-Bases and Roadbases

1.   Unbound sub-bases and roadbases shall be constructed using granular material Type 1 or Type 2 in accordance with Clause 363. Roadbase material may be replaced by any of the materials specified for the pavement courses to be superimposed on it.

2.   Frost susceptible material as defined in the test method and procedure of the Transport and Road Research Laboratory Supplementary Report No. SR 829, shall not be used within 450 mm of the final road surface.

3.   Unbound material up to 225 mm compacted thickness shall be spread in one layer. Unbound material of compacted thickness greater than 225 mm shall be laid in two or more layers and the minimum compacted thickness of any such layer shall be 110 mm. Where layers of unbound material are of unequal thickness the lowest layer shall be the thickest layer.

4.   Compaction shall be completed as soon as possible after the material has been spread and in accordance with Table 1100A. Care shall be taken to obtain full compaction in the vicinity of both longitudinal and transverse joints.

5.   On completion of compaction and immediately before overlaying the surface of any layer of material shall be well closed, free from ridges, cracks, loose material, pot holes, ruts and other defects.

1106.   Road Pavements, Bituminous Bound Materials

1.   Bituminous bound pavement courses shall be constructed using materials in accordance with Clause 305. Aggregates shall be clean, hard and durable.

2.   Bituminous materials shall be transported in clean insulated vehicles and shall be covered over when in transit or awaiting tipping. The use of dust, coated dust or water on the interior of the vehicles to facilitate discharge shall be kept to a minimum and any excess shall be removed by tipping or brushing.

3.   Materials shall be spread, levelled and tamped by an approved self-propelled paving machine. As soon as possible after arrival at the site the mixed material shall be laid without delay. It shall be supplied at a rate of delivery that will enable the paver to operate continuously.

4.   The rate of travel of the paver and its method of operation shall be adjusted to ensure an even and uniform flow of material across the full laying width with freedom from dragging or tearing and without segregation of material.

5.   The material shall be laid in compliance with the British Standard appropriate for that material or otherwise in compliance with BS 594.

6.   Hand laying of bituminous material shall not be carried out except in the following circumstances.

   (a)   For laying regulating course of irregular shape and varying thickness, or

(b)   in confined spaces where it is impracticable for a paver to operate, or

(c)   for footways, or

(d)   for laying mastic asphalt in complying with BS 1447.

7.   The minimum thickness of material laid in one pass of the paver shall be 90 mm or the full course thickness where this is less than 90 mm.

8.   Material shall be uniformly compacted as soon as rolling can be effected without causing undue displacement of the mixed material and shall be substantially completed while the temperature is greater than the minimum rolling temperature stated in the appropriate British Standard. Rolling shall continue until all roller marks have been removed.

9.   Compaction shall be carried out using smooth wheeled rollers having a mass per metre width of roll of 4400 to 6000 kg and a width of roll not less than 450 mm.

10.   The material shall be rolled in a longitudinal direction with the driven rolls nearest the paver. The roller shall first compact the material adjacent to any joints and then work from the lower to the upper side of the layer, overlapping on successive passes by at least half the width of the rear roll.

11.   Rollers shall not stand on newly laid material while there is a risk that the surface will be deformed.

12.   Coated chippings shall be evenly applied to the wearing course by an approved mechanical spreader. Addition of chippings by hand shall not be carried out except in the following circumstances:-

(a)   In confined spaces where it is impracticable for a chipping spreader to operate, or

(b)   as a temporary expedient when adjustments have to be made to the spreader, or

(c)   where hand laying of the wearing course is in progress, or

(d)   to correct unevenness in the distribution of chippings.

13.   All chippings shall be rolled into the wearing course in such a manner that they are effectively held.

14.   Hand raking of wearing course material laid by a paver and the addition of such material by hand spreading for adjustment of level shall not be carried out except at the edges of layers of material and at gullies and manholes.

15.   At joints in wearing courses, the material shall be fully compacted and the exposed edge cut back for a distance equal to the specified layer thickness to form a vertical face. All loosened material shall be discarded and the vertical face coated with a suitable grade of hot tar or hot bitumen before the next section is laid.

16.   All joints shall be offset at least 300 mm from parallel joints in the layer beneath and in an approved layout.

17.   Where directed a bituminous spray tack coat shall be applied to the surface on which laying is to take place.

18.   Upper roadbase material or basecourse material shall not remain uncovered by the wearing course or surface treatment for more than three consecutive days after being laid.

19.   Regulating course material shall be made and laid in accordance with the requirements for one or other of the specified bituminous roadbase materials.

1107. Wet Mix Macadam

1. The materials for wet mix macadam shall be in accordance with Clause 305.

2. Unless otherwise approved the materials shall be mixed in a mixer complying with BS 1305.

3. Wet mix macadam shall be spread evenly on the sub-base and compacted in layers of not more than 200 mm thickness at the optimum moisture content ±0.5% as determined in compliance with BS 5835.

1108. Surface Dressing

1. Surface dressing shall be carried out in accordance with the Transport and Road Research Laboratory Road Note 39.

2. The materials for surface dressing shall be in accordance with Clause 305.

3. Spraying of the binder shall not commence until preliminary patching of the surface is complete. The surface shall be generally dry and free of standing water.

4. Metal fittings in the road surface shall be protected before the binder is applied to prevent adherence of the surface dressing. The protection shall be removed before the road is opened to use.

5. Chippings shall be uniformly spread by a mechanical spreader. Any thinly chipped areas shall have additional chippings spread by hand.

6. Chippings specified to be hot shall be applied at a temperature within the range of 60°C to 120°C depending on the ambient air temperature.

7. For tar or bitumen coated chippings the percentage of binder for the coating shall be within the range of 0.5 to 1.2% by mass in accordance with the size of chippings being used.

8. Chippings shall be rolled into the binder by an approved pneumatic tyred multiwheeled roller.

9. Traffic shall not be permitted to run on any newly surface dressed area without approval.

10. Aftercare and opening of the road to traffic shall comply with Road Note 39. Chippings displaced by traffic shall be swept up and removed at regular intervals.

1109. Concrete Roads and Hardstandings

   1. Base

   (a) The base shall consist of granular material laid to a minimum compacted thickness of 75 mm in accordance with Clause 1105 for sub-base. Where the formation material is frost susceptible the base shall have a minimum compacted thickness of 300 mm and its surface shall comply with the tolerance specified for roadbase in Clause 1102.

2. Separation Membrane

   (a) A separation membrane shall be provided between the concrete surface slab and sub-base.

   (b) The membrane shall be polythene sheet or waterproof paper in accordance with Clause 372, lapped 300 mm at joints. Precautions shall be taken to prevent ponding on the membrane.

3. Concrete Pavement
   (a) The pavement shall be reinforced concrete with transverse and longitudinal joints as *required by the Contract.*

(b)   The concrete shall be Grade C40 using Ordinary Portland cement minimum cement content of 320 kg/m3[3]. Aggregates shall be of nominal size not exceeding 40 mm. The water content shall be the minimum required to achieve full compaction of the concrete. The maximum free water cement ratio shall be 0.50.

(c)   For air entrained concrete the total quantity of entrained air shall be 4.5% by volume and be within the tolerances given in BS 5328. The air content shall be determined in accordance with BS 1881 at least 6 times per day at the point of delivery to the paving plant.

(d)   Side forms for slabs shall be of steel, or timber if approved, drilled as required for dowel bars. They shall be straight, within a tolerance of 3 mm in 3 m and free of warps or of appropriate radius for curves of 30 m radius of less. As an alternative for curved work, 5 mm steel plates supported by not less than three pins for every 3 m of length may be used. Forms shall be sufficiently rigid to prevent movement during laying and compacting the concrete.

(e)   Forms shall be cleaned and oiled before each use.

(f)   The forms shall be bedded on low water content cement mortar or concrete Grade C7.5 and set to the pavement surface level within a tolerance of ±3 mm. The bedding shall not extend under the slab. The vertical step between the ends of adjacent forms shall be not greater than 3 mm. The horizontal alignment of forms shall be within a tolerance of ±10 mm of the required alignment of the pavement edge. The mortar or concrete bedding shall be broken out after use.

(g)   To allow adequate time for checking the forms the Contractor shall give the Engineer not less than 24 hours notice of his intention to place concrete. Side forms shall not be removed less than 12 hours after placing the concrete. Forms shall be removed in a manner which will not cause damage to the concrete or projecting tie bars.

4.   Steel Reinforcement
   (a)   Reinforcement shall be free of oil, dirt, loose rust or scale.

   (b)   Laps in longitudinal bars shall be not less that 35 bar diameters or 450 mm whichever is greater. At laps between prefabricated sheets the first transverse bar of one sheet shall lie within the last complete mesh of the previous sheet.

   (c)   Laps in any transverse reinforcement shall be a minimum of 300 mm. Where prefabricated reinforcement sheets are used and longitudinal and transverse laps coincide, no lap is required in the transverse bars within the lap of the longitudinal reinforcement. These transverse bars may be cropped or fabricated shorter so that the requirements for cover are met.

   (d)   Reinforcement positioned prior to concreting shall be fixed on approved supports and secured to ensure that the required cover is achieved.

   (e)   Reinforcement assembled on site shall be tied or fixed in an approved manner at sufficient intersections to provide rigidity.

5.   Joints in Concrete Pavements
   (a)   Joints shall be constructed by approved methods and have vertical faces. Sealing grooves in the surface of the concrete at joints shall be formed during the construction of the slab or, where concrete is continued across the line of the joint, sawn in the concrete when sufficiently hard to produce a clean cut.

   (b)   Transverse joints shall extend to the full width of the slab and shall be in a straight line at right angles to the longitudinal axis of the slab. Where the pavement is constructed in two or more widths, corresponding joints on either side of a longitudinal joint shall be in line with each other.

6.   Expansion Joints

(a)   Expansion joints shall be formed at the intervals *required by the Contract*. Joints shall be filled to within 25 mm of the top with an approved premoulded filler complying with Clause 349. The sealing groove, 25 mm deep, shall be 6 mm greater in width than the thickness of the filler. The joint filler thickness shall comply with Clause 349 or shall be the thickness *required by the Contract*.

(b)   Dowel bars shall be provided at 300 mm centres at mid depth of slab, parallel to the finished surface and to the longitudinal axis. They shall be in accordance with Clause 318. The projecting half of each dowel bar shall be coated with a thin film of bond breaking compound complying with Clause 307 and provided with a close fitting sleeve 100 mm long of waterproofed cardboard or other approved material. The end of the sleeve will be capped with a disc of joint filler or pad of cotton waste to a depth of 25mm. The assembly of joint filler and dowel bars shall be suported so as to remain in the correct position while the concrete is being placed and compacted. Dowel bars shall not deviate from their required alignment by more than 6 mm per 300 mm length of bar.

7.   Contraction Joints

(a)   Contraction joints shall be formed at the intervals *required by the Contract*. They shall be similar to expansion joints except that the filler shall be replaced by a timber fillet, 75 mm by 40 mm, fixed firmly to the base, and the dowel bar caps shall be omitted. The sealing groove shall be 25 mm deep by 12 mm wide, located vertically above the fillet to within a tolerance of ±12 mm. Where the joint is formed at a cross form as in alternative bay construction or at the end of concreting for the day, the timber fillet shall be omitted.

8.   Longitudinal Joints

(a)   Longitudinal joints shall be formed in all concrete roads exceeding 4.5 m in width and in other paved areas as *required by the Contract*. Where concrete is placed continuously over the line of a longitudinal joint a timber fillet 75 mm x 40 mm shall be cast into the base of the slab except where the joint is a vertical butt joint between two slabs. Steel tie bars 12 mm dia. by 1 m long bedded for the full length directly in the concrete to develop complete bond shall be set symmetrically across the line of the joint at 600 mm centres, at mid depth of the slab.

9.   Placing and Compacting

(a)   Placing, compacting and finishing the concrete shall be carried out as rapidly as possible. Transverse sections of concrete shall be fully compacted throughout the whole depth and finished within two hours of completion of mixing the first batch of concrete in that section.

(b)   Concrete shall be continuous up to prescribed transverse joints. Intermediate construction joints shall not be permitted except in the event of mechanical breakdown or adverse weather. If concreting is stopped at an intermediate point the concrete shall be finished off vertically on a transverse line to full depth. Before placing concrete against a surface that is set the surface shall be scabbled, loose and porous concrete removed and the surface wetted.

(c)   Where reinforcement has not been fixed in advance of concreting a first layer of concrete shall be placed so as to give the required thickness after compaction to ensure the required top cover to the reinforcement. The reinforcement shall then be placed by hand, or approved mechanical means, and covered with concrete which shall be compacted to finished levels. Compaction shall be by one or more passes of an approved hand guided mechanically vibrated beam.

10.   Surface Finish

(a)   Immediately after the final pass of the compacting beam the surface of the concrete shall be brushed transversely to produce a lightly brush marked surface finish. Joints shall have a 100 mm arris trowelled finish on each side.

(b)   Surface irregularities shall not exceed 5 mm when checked with a three metre straight edge.

11. Curing
   (a)   Finished concrete surfaces shall be sprayed immediately with an approved tinted resinous curing compound at a rate of approximately 0.25 litres per sq m using a low pressure fine spray. Curing compound shall be prevented from entering joint grooves. Concrete shall be protected for not less than 2 hours after placing from the effects of sunshine or rain by opaque waterproof covers, kept clear of the surface, to shed water away from fresh concrete.

12. Sealing of Joint Grooves
   (a)   Not less than 14 days after the concrete has been placed joint grooves shall be sealed as *required by the Contract*. Dust, grit and temporary protective materials shall be removed and the groove dried immediately prior to permanent sealing. Sealants shall be applied in accordance with the manufacturer's instructions.

   (b)   In summer joint grooves shall be filled with sealing compound flush with the surface of the slabs. In winter they shall be filled to a level 5 mm below slab surface.

13. Manholes, Gullies and Service Chambers
   (a)   Manhole covers, frames and surface boxes shall be set in separate slabs of a size which matches the exterior dimensions of the shaft or chamber. Where practicable the slabs shall have sides parallel to the longitudinal and transverse joints. They shall be cast after the concrete pavement, against 20 mm thick expansion joint filler placed along the exposed pavement sides. A groove 20 mm deep by 15 mm wide shall be provided and sealed. The slabs shall be of the same concrete grade as the adjacent pavement and reinforced as *required by the Contract*.

   (b)   Gully frames within the paved area shall be separated from the concrete by a chase not less than 3 mm thick filled with sealing compound.

14. Sett String Course
   (a)   Where *required by the Contract* a row of granite or whinstone setts shall be laid at the end of a concrete roadway where it meets one of different construction. The setts shall be not less than 100 mm deep by 150 mm wide laid on a 150 mm by 115 mm foundation of Grade C20 concrete. They shall be bedded and jointed in 1:3 cement sand mortar with their surfaces flush with the surface of the concrete.

1110. Kerbs and Footways
1. Precast Concrete Kerbs, Edgings and Quadrants
   (a)   Precast kerbs, edgings and quadrants shall be laid and bedded in 1:3 cement sand mortar not less than 13 mm thick either on the concrete carriageway or a concrete foundation or haunch constructed as required by the contract. They shall be backed with Grade C20 concrete.

   (b)   Where kerbs are laid on concrete carriageways, joints with filler complying with Clause 1109.6 shall be provided with kerbs coincident with the carriageway expansion joints.

   (c)   For radii of 12 m or less, kerbs of appropriate radius shall be used.

   (d)   Any units of kerb edging and quadrant shall not deviate more than 3 mm from the line and level at either end.

2. Footways
   (a)   The formation shall have any hollows made up, soft areas replaced with hard graded filling and shall be thoroughly compacted by a 2.5 tonnes roller.

(b)   The undercourse shall be one of the following materials compacted to a thickness of 100 mm by a 2.5 tonnes roller;-

   (i)   Sub-base material complying with Clause 362.

   (ii)   65 mm nominal size aggregate complying with BS 882 Table 1, blinded with approved material, watered if required, and rolled to compaction.

3.   Footways, Flexible Surfacing

   (a)   The flexible surfacing shall be laid to levels and cross falls *required by the Contract*, compacted by a 2.5 tonnes roller to the thickness stated and shall comprise:-

      (i)   a bitumen macadam basecourse 38 mm thick to Clause 1106, and

      (ii)   a wearing course 20 mm thick of bitumen macadam or fine cold asphalt complying with Clause 1106. Fine cold asphalt shall be dressed with chippings complying with Clause 305.9 spread evenly at a rate of 6 kg per sq m, rolled into the surface immediately prior to the final roll of the asphalt.

4.   Footways, Concrete Paved

   (a)   Precast concrete slabs shall comply with Clause 347, be laid to the required cross falls and bedded *as required by the Contract*. The slabs shall be laid to a 150 mm bond or 300 mm bond as *required by the Contract*, with joints at right angles to the kerb.

   (b)   On circular work where the radius is 12 m or less all slabs shall be radially cut on both edges to the required line.

Minor Electrical
Installations

1201. General
1. All apparatus and wiring shall be suitable for use with a 3 phase 4 wire 415/240 V 50 Hz earthed neutral supply system.
2. The installation shall comply with the following:-
   (a)   The Regulations for Electrical Installations, issued by the Institution of Electrical Engineers.

   (b)   The Building Regulations.

   (c)   The requirements of the local Electricity Board.

   (d)   The Electricity Supply Regulations 1988.

   (e)   The Electricity at Work Regulations 1989.

1202. Armoured Cables
1. Cables shall be suitable for 600/1000 volts and shall comply with BS 6346. The cross sectional area of the conductor of any cable shall not be less than 1.5 mm^2.

2. Cables shall have copper conductors and shall be PVC insulated, PVC sheathed, single wire armoured and have an extruded PVC sheath over the armouring wires.

3. The installation of multicore cable shall comply with Appendix B of BS 6346. Terminations shall be made with a clamping gland of an approved pattern, the gland being complete with PVC shroud.

4. Any joints in PVC/SWA/PVC cables shall be made using proprietary joint kits in accordance with the manufacturer's instructions.

5. Armoured PVC insulated cables installed in buildings shall be in ducts or fastened by saddles to galvanised cable trays fixed to walls or ceilings or secured to walls by approved cable cleats.

1203. Non-Armoured Cables
1. PVC insulated cables for drawing into conduits shall be 600/1000 volt grade, single core, the core having a minimum cross sectional area of 1.5 mm^2(1/1.38mm) and shall comply with BS 6004.

2. Burrs shall be removed from conduits before cables are drawn into them.

3. Cables shall be in complete lengths between terminations. If joints are permitted they shall be made with a shrouded porcelain connector fixed within a box of adequate size. After making the joint all holes in the connector block shall be filled with a non-hygroscopic insulating compound.

1204. Cables, Mineral Insulated Copper Sheathed
1. All M.I.C.S. cables shall be 1,000 V heavy duty grade, over-sheathed with orange coloured PVC and shall comply with BS 6207:Part 1.

2. Fittings and terminations shall comply with BS 6081.

3. Before installation M.I.C.S. cable shall be tested for insulation resistance and if below the manufacturer's required standard it shall be warmed by a suitable means to expel any moisture. Should this prove ineffective the cable shall not be used. If a cable has to be left unconnected for a period of time it shall be adequately supported and the end made off with a dummy pot seal to prevent mechanical damage and the ingress of moisture.

4. Sealing pots shall be supplied marked with the appropriate cable reference and shall be of the screw on type. Compression type pots shall not be used.

5.   Insulating sleeving shall be supplied marked with the appropriate nominal cross sectional area of the conductor.

6.   M.I.C.S. cables shall be complete lengths between terminations.

7.   All pot seals shall be securely fitted and filled with compound to exclude air and moisture.

8.   M.I.C.S. cable tails shall be properly finished with correctly anchored neoprene sleeving. Where the cables terminate at equipment subject to vibration and at all starters, relays and the like sufficient allowance shall be made in the lengths of the cables to enable glands with tails to be withdrawn from the equipment without damaging the cables and adequate antivibration loops shall be left in the cable runs. PVC shrouds shall be fitted to all glands.

9.   All cables shall be properly dressed using tools supplied by the cable manufacturer for that purpose to ensure that the cables are free from kinks, and the whole installation has a neat and workmanlike appearance.

10.   M.I.C.S. cables shall be fixed to cable trays of approved pattern or secured by saddles to surfaces at intervals of not more than 450 mm. Saddles shall be secured to steelwork by mild steel screws with steel washers and nuts or to other surfaces by brass woodscrews. Saddles and fixing straps shall be of bronze or similar approved material with PVC sheathing.

11.   M.I.C.S. cables shall not be buried directly in concrete, floor or wall finishes, or behind plaster. Where cables pass through walls, floors, platforms or the like they shall be protected by a galvanised metal sleeving or conduit projecting 200 mm beyond the finished surfaces.

1205.   Armoured Cables Laid Underground

1.   Underground cables shall be laid in trenches either in sand or in ducts as *required by the Contract*. Where laid in sand they shall be bedded on sand 75 mm thick measured from the bottom of the trench and immediately after laying the cable shall be covered with not less than 75 mm of sand. Cables shall be protected by interlocking cable tiles of approved size and type lain on top of the sand or by yellow plastic tape printed with "Danger Electric Cable" laid above the cables at a depth not exceeding 200 mm below final ground level, as *required by the Contract*. Cables shall be tested before laying tiles or final backfilling.

2.   Cable trenches shall be not less than 700 mm deep measured from the final surface of the ground or as *required by the Contract*.

3.   Ducts shall be laid with a cover of not less than 700 mm measured from the surface of the ground or as *required by the Contract*. Suitable drawcords shall be inserted within the ducts. The dimensions and material of the ducting shall be as *required by the Contract*.

4.   Except as required above, backfilling of the cable trenches shall be carried out in accordance with the provisions of Clause 515.

5.   Immediately after backfilling precast concrete cable markers of an approved design shall be fixed adjacent to the trench. Each marker shall have a metal plate securely attached indicating the class and depth of each cable. Markers shall be at points not more than 25 m apart, at through and tee joints, branches and changes of direction.

6.   The minimum spacing of cables in trenches shall comply with Table 1200A.

7.   Access chambers shall be provided at intervals of and dimensions as *required by the Contract*.

8.   Except for very long routes the cable shall be supplied and installed in one length. Where this is not possible proprietary joints carried out in accordance with the manufacturer's instructions will be permitted and shall be located within suitably identified access chambers.

TABLE 1200A Minimum spacing of Cables in Trenches

Cable	Low Voltage mm	Telephone Control or Coaxial mm	Gas, Water and other piped services mm	High Voltage mm
Low Voltage	25	150	300	600
Telephone,Control or Coaxial	150	50	275	600

9.   Each cable end shall terminate in a suitable compression type gland incorporating an armour clamp for earth continuity and sealing ring suitable for damp situations, all enclosed within a PVC shroud.

1206.   Motor Installations and Cabling to Motors

1.   Where practicable all motors shall be provided with anticondensation heaters rated for 240 V 50 Hz connected within the motor terminal box, the cover of which shall bear a warning "Motor heater fitted - Isolate before opening".

2.   Where plant or machinery is driven by an electric motor there shall be means at hand for stopping the plant or machinery when necessary to prevent danger. If the motor starter is not adjacent to the machine weatherproof lock stop stations shall be provided, as necessary for the purpose of stopping the motor. Lock-stop buttons shall be coloured red and shall be of the lock off type, labelled "Emergency Stop". Lock stop stations shall be provided with equipment to prevent the accidental or inadvertent starting of the motor.

3.   Cables to motors shall be terminated in cable changing boxes mounted on the motor plinth or other suitable adjacent point. Final connections to the motor shall comprise PVC insulated cable in PVC covered flexible conduit. A separate circuit protective conductor, complying with relevant section of the IEE Regulations for Electrical Installations, shall be provided within the flexible conduit.

4.   Local isolators installed adjacent to motors may be used as the cable changing boxes. Heater connections shall be made in a similar manner to the main motor connections. Connections into motors having insulation of Class B or higher grade, as defined in BS 2757, shall be made using glass strand insulation in PVC covered flexible conduit.

1207.   Conduit Systems and Fittings

1.   Steel conduit and fittings shall be screwed galvanised heavy gauge steel or malleable cast iron complying with BS 4568.

2.   PVC conduit and fittings shall be rigid or flexible complying with BS 4607.

3.   The minimum size of conduit shall be 20 mm diameter.

4.   Conduits buried in plaster or brick, block or concrete walls shall have not less than 20 mm of cover. Conduit ends shall be securely plugged and boxes shall have covers fitted prior to plastering.

5.   Steel conduit laid in concrete shall be coated on the outside with an approved anticorrosive coating, the screw threads being left bright. After installation and before making good the exposed threads shall be similarly coated.

6.   The use of inspection or plain elbows and tees will not be permitted. Circular junction boxes shall be used where these would otherwise be required.

7.   Conduit entries to galvanised sheet steel switch enclosures shall be made by means of brass hexagonal smooth bore bushes, serrated washers and couplings.

8.   Surface conduit systems in galvanised steel conduit shall be installed with a minimum of exposed threads. All threads left exposed and any parts sustaining damage during installation shall be coated with an approved anticorrosive coating.

9.   Surface runs in steel or plastic conduit shall be securely fixed by distance spacing saddles at intervals of not more than 1.2 m and at not more than 300 mm from the centre of each bend, junction box or accessory. Box lids shall be fitted with gaskets and junction boxes exposed to the weather or to damp or corrosive atmosphere shall be filled with non-hygroscopic plastic sealing compound.

10.   Outlet and junction boxes on surface systems shall be fixed by at least two screws.

1208.   Single Phase Switches and Switched Socket Outlets
1.   Switches and switched socket outlets are shown in general location in the Contract. Final positions of these items shall be determined on site by the Engineer.

2.   Unless otherwise *required by the Contract*, all switches shall be mounted 1350 mm above finished floor level. Switched socket outlets shall be mounted at 450 mm or 1350 mm above finished floor level as *required by the Contract*.

1209.   Switches and Socket Outlets - 240 V
1.   All accessories shall be from the matching range of a single manufacturer, flush or surface mounted as *required by the Contract*.

2.   Switches shall be single pole with a substantial actuating toggle of an insulating material, the whole being enclosed within a metal enclosure, and shall comply with BS 3676.

3.   Switches for mounting in plaster shall have an enclosure of heavy pressed galvanised steel covered with a white insulating switch plate fixed to the enclosure with separate screws. Where more than three switches are to be grouped into one position a demountable grid type of switch unit shall be used. Switch toggles shall be of the rocker pattern.

4.   Switched socket outlets shall comply with BS 1363. Switch toggles shall be of the rocker pattern.

5.   Spur boxes shall incorporate double pole switches and neon indicators and shall be fitted with rocker type operating toggles.

6.   All fused connection units shall be switched, have a single pole fuse link and shall comply with BS 1362.

7.   Switches for single phase water heaters shall be double pole type of 20 A rating with neon indicators and shall be engraved 'Water Heater'.

8.   Switches for use with thermal storage radiators shall be of the double pole type of 25 A rating. Where the heaters incorporate a fan they shall have twin double pole switches and cord outlets labelled 'Heater' and 'Fan' respectively. The switch shall be fitted with a thermostat looping terminal and neon indicators.

9.   Fused connector boxes for use with electric clocks shall be fully recessed and terminals shall be suitable for 2.5 mm conductors. Provision for supporting the clock shall be provided on the connector.

10.   Cooker control units shall comply with BS 4177.

11.   Surface mounted switches and switched socket outlets shall be fitted with plates of heavy gauge steel with a durable finish. Boxes for surface mounting switches and switched socket outlets shall be of a similar finish to the switch or socket.

12.   Where flush and surface mounting equipment is used in the same room, surface cabling shall be carried out using mineral insulated PVC covered cable.

13.   Switches and switched socket outlets exposed to weather or damp or corrosive atmospheres shall be single pole tumbler switches with a brass toggle actuated by a disc with a rotary action. The switch shall be enclosed within a weatherproof galvanised steel or malleable cast iron case. Switched socket outlets shall comply with BS 4343 and shall have three contact cover tubes, the socket outlet and switch being housed in a weatherproof galvanised cast iron case. The switch and socket outlet shall be interlocked so that the plug must be pushed fully home before the switch can be closed and the plug cannot be withdrawn with the switch in the closed position. The socket outlet shall be provided with a captive brass screw cap fitted with rubber gaskets to prevent the ingress of moisture when the plug is not in position.

14.   Socket outlets for equipment which will be used in damp conditions or external to the building shall be provided with a residual current device of the two pole type with a maximum tripping current of 30 mA.

15.   Plugs for use with socket outlets described in Clause 1209.13 shall have brass cases with a captive locking ring and earthing screws. The cable shall enter the plug through a screwed brass packing gland which shall form an integral part of the case.

1210.   Socket Outlets 110 V, 415 V and Portable Equipment
1.   Socket outlets for use with portable hand tools, small pumps and inspection lamps on 110 V 50 Hz centre tap earth systems shall comply with BS 4343. Socket outlets shall be rated at 16 A unless otherwise *required by the Contract*.

2.   Socket outlets for use on 415 V 50 Hz 3 phase and neutral systems shall comply with BS 4343, and shall be rated at 32 A unless otherwise shown. The socket outlets shall be interlocked with an adjacent switch such that the plug may neither be inserted nor withdrawn with the switch in the closed position.

3.   Where the Contract requires that provision be made for supplies to portable equipment direct from socket outlets the supplies shall be rated at 110 V 50 Hz, centre tap earth. The voltage shall be derived from the transformers of 1kVA continuous rating or larger, as *required by the Contract*. The output shall be taken to double pole miniature circuit breakers of rating 20 A each supplying a maximum of four socket outlets to BS 4343.

4.   Where the Contract does not require that provision be made for supplies to portable equipment by means of socket outlets as specified in Clause 1210 portable hand tools and equipment shall be suitable for operation on 110 V 50 Hz. The supply shall be derived from portable shrouded transformer units of 1kVA rating or larger, as *required by the Contract* to BS 4363 fed from 240 V socket outlets.

1211.   Starters
1.   Starters provided for installation with electric motors shall be of the automatic contactor type and shall comply with BS 4941. Contactors shall comply with BS 5424 for utilisation category AC3 and shall be magnetically operated. Contacts shall be of a replaceable pattern, and each phase shall be provided with deep arc chutes of arc proof material not normally in contact with live metal parts.

114

2.   All starter units shall be fitted with a fault making, load breaking, isolating switch complying with BS 5419. Isolating switches shall have independent manual operation, be suitable for uninterrupted duty and utilisation category AC 3, and be interlocked with the starter doors. Provision shall be made for padlocking the isolating switches in the "OFF" position.

3.   Starters incorporating two or more contactors shall have each contactor labelled as to its function. All relays operating in conjunction with the starter shall be similarly labelled.

4.   Operating push buttons shall be coloured and engraved or labelled as to their function in accordance with BS 4099.

5.   Selector switches shall be of the fully rotary pattern with positive location in the various selected positions and shall be suitably labelled.

6.   Starters for motors of 1.5 kw and above shall be fitted with ammeters. Starters for motors below 1.5 kw shall be fitted with red pilot lamps.

7.   Ammeters shall be of industrial grade. Scales shall be from 0-150%-500% full load current. The portion of scale between 0-150% shall be suitably graduated and occupy approximately two thirds of the full scale deflection of the meter. The portion between 150%-500% shall be ungraduated and damped.

8.   Where *required by the Contract* digital hours run indicators showing up to 100,000 hours shall be fitted to starters.

9.   Starters shall be provided with thermostatically controlled anticondensation heaters of the totally enclosed pattern. The heaters shall be electrically interlocked with the starter door, so that the equipment will be isolated when the door is opened.

1212.   Isolating Switches, Switch Fuses and Fuse Switches, Distribution Boards and Busbar Chambers

1.   Isolating switches for rated currents not exceeding 200 A shall comply with BS 5419. Units shall comprise air break switches, contained within a metal enclosure having a cover interlocked with the switch mechanism such that the switch interior is inaccessible when the switch is closed. A device giving a clear and positive indication of the position of the switch shall be provided, this indication being clearly apparent from the normal operating position. The covers of the isolator enclosure shall comply with BS 5419, IP54 or better.

2.   Switches providing isolation local to motors shall be fully rated to safely break 150% of the normal full load current of the associated motor and to withstand the short circuit load of that motor. Fully rotary isolators may be used without interlocked covers in this application if approved in writing. When non-interlocked isolators are used a large clear warning label complying with Clause 1214 shall state that isolation must be made elsewhere.

3.   Switch fuses and fuse switches shall comply with BS 88 and BS 5419.

4.   Fuse switches shall be of the parallel action double break pattern with the fuse elements readily accessible for maintenance, inspection and replacement. Covers shall be interlocked with the switch mechanism in such a manner that access to the unit cannot be gained unless the switch is in the open position and the switch cannot be closed unless the cover is securely closed. Clear and positive indication of the position of the switch shall be provided in such a position that it is readily visible from the normal operating position. Moving contacts shall be removable for maintenance and fixed contacts shall be fully shrouded.

5.   Distribution boards shall be suitable for either HRC fuses or miniature circuit breakers as *required by the Contract*. Where suitable for HRC fuses distribution boards shall be fully shrouded to BS 5486.
Where suitable for miniature circuit breakers distribution boards shall be dust and damp protected to comply with BS 5486.

6.   A printed schedule of circuits shall be permanently fixed within the door of each distribution board and shall be completed and approved prior to commissioning. The schedule shall be protected by means of perspex sheeting or similar approved means. All units shall be fitted with identification labels clearly indicating their function.

7.   Where enclosures are fabricated from sheet steel it shall be not less than 2 mm thick and shall be protected against corrosion by an approved metallizing process. Doors and covers of the units shall be fitted with suitable gaskets to comply with the IP 54 classification of BS 5490. Enclosures shall be fitted with undrilled detachable gland plates and gaskets. Knockouts will not be permitted.

8.   Busbars and busbar connections shall comply with BS 159.

1213.   Fuses
1.   Fuse elements shall comply with BS 88.

2.   All switch, fuse and starter gear shall be provided complete with one set of spare fuses of each rating used, carried in holders located in the door of the appropriate cubicle if possible.

1214.   Labels
1.   Labels shall be manufactured from colourless transparent plastic material not less than 3 mm thick. The label shall be bevelled on the four front edges and the letters shall be engraved on the back of the label. Countersunk holes shall be formed and chromium plated instrument head screws shall be used to fix the label to its unit.

2.   Labels for use as nameplates shall have the letters filled in white and the back sprayed black to give white lettering on a black background.

3.   Labels for use as warnings shall have the letters filled in white and the underside sprayed red to given white lettering on a red background.

4.   The minimum height of characters used in labels shall be 6 mm.

5.   Alternative labelling systems such as laminated plastic may be used if approved in writing.

6.   A schedule of labels shall be submitted for approval prior to manufacture.

7.   All labels shall be fixed to equipment prior to commissioning tests being carried out.

8.   All cables, except final distribution to lighting and accessories shall be allocated a number under the Contract, and shall be permanently marked by approved means at all maintenance access points such as joint boxes, drawpits or chambers, and where they leave and enter ducts.

1215.   Internal and External Lighting
1.   Unless otherwise *required by the Contract* light fittings shall comply with Table 1200B.

2.   Emergency lights shall be provided at staircases and exit doors to indicate escape routes as *required by the Contract*. These shall be 3 hour non-maintained emergency light fitting with 300 mm 8 watt white lamp. Where damp conditions occur waterproof fittings shall be used. Emergency lights at exit doors shall bear the legend 'EXIT' or 'EMERGENCY EXIT' as appropriate.

1216.   Earthing
Particular attention is drawn to the provisions in respect of earthing in the IEE Regulations.
1.   All metalwork, other than current carrying parts of electrical circuits, forming part of the

TABLE 1200B

	Location	Type of Fitting
i)	Motor rooms, switch rooms and other dry areas	1.8 m or 2.4 m single or double fluorescent fitting with quick start or electronic gear and industrial metal reflector.
ii)	Pump rooms, dry wells underground chambers. Rooms liable to flooding or general damp conditions. Toilets, shower rooms etc.	Bulkhead fitting with 28W or 38W 2-D or 18W PL type fluorescent fitting.
iii)	Offices and messrooms	1.8 m or 2.4 m single or double fluorescent fitting with quickstart or electronic gear and prismatic diffuser.
iv)	External wall mounted lights	70W SON fitting complete with alloy or polycarbonate enclosure.

installation shall be efficiently connected to the works main earthing system. Metalwork shall include the casings of motors, starters, transformers, relays, switch and fusegear, distribution boards, conduit, trunking, traywork, cable sheaths, armouring, ducts, boxes, light fittings and the like.

2.   All conductive parts such as pipework access ladders, walkways, tanks and the like shall be bonded to comply with the IEE Regulations.

3.   Items of equipment such as light fittings, distribution boards and the like shall be bonded to earth by means of a separate insulated earthing conductor or, where approved in writing, cable sheaths or conduits. Trunking or tray work shall not be used as an earth continuity conductor.

1217.   Testing
1.   Cables laid underground shall be tested for insulation resistance, continuity and earth continuity immediately before and immediately after trenches are backfilled. Joints which prove faulty shall be remade and retested.

2.   On completion of the installation all circuits shall be proved to be correct and the whole installation shall be tested in accordance with the requirements of the Contract, the Regulations for Electrical Installations issued by the Institution of Electrical Engineers.

3.   The testing shall be carried out in the presence of the Engineer or his representative.

4.   The Contractor shall provide all necessary labour, supervision, apparatus and instruments for the tests. The Engineer shall be at liberty to use any instrument or testing apparatus that he may consider necessary to carry out the prescribed tests. The Contractor shall, if required give evidence of the accuracy of any testing apparatus and instrument.

5.   Any faults and defects shall be remedied by the Contractor and retesting carried out as directed.

1218.   General
1.   Rubber matting to BS 921 shall be provided in front of all switchboards.

2.   An approved framed notice giving details of treatment for electric shock shall be permanently fixed adjacent to any electrical switchboards.

1219. Record Drawings
1.   The Contractor shall supply a set of negatives showing in approved manner a complete record of as installed work.

2.   Upon completion of the Contract the Contractor shall provide a framed distribution diagram mounted adjacent to the main switchboard and shall also provide details of the installation design as required by the IEE regulations for electrical installations.

1220. Return to Site
1.   Six months after the installation has been taken over, each circuit shall be retested by the Contractor in the presence of the Engineer or his representative. The Contractor shall trace all faults and replace any material found defective.

Tunnelling and Pipejacking

1301. Health and Safety

1.   The Contractor shall comply with BS 6164 "Safety in tunnelling in the Construction Industry" and Health and Safety Executive Guidance Note EH40 which provides Occupational Exposure Limits and other recommended minimum standards.

1302. Ventilation and Atmospheric Environment

1.   Air shall be supplied by forced ventilation. Provision shall be made for a supply of at least 4 m^3 per minute of air per 1 kW of diesel or equivalent plant working in the heading, to be discharged at each working face. This is in addition to air which is required for ventilation and removal of gases and dust.

2.   In underground workings and in confined spaces the air breathed by persons shall contain not less than 19% of oxygen by volume (dry basis).

3.   In rock excavation all drill holes shall be wet drilled to control dust in the air.

4.   No smoking, or open flames, shall be permitted in any part of the underground works.

5.   Atmospheric pollutants such as noxious gases, vapours and dusts shall be carefully controlled so that the levels of concentration do not constitute a hazard to human life and health and shall not exceed the Occupational Exposure Limits referred to in BS 6164 and Guidance Note EH40. Where more than one pollutant is present the Occupational Exposure Limit for each pollutant shall be reduced as approved.

6.   Inflammable vapours and gases shall be strictly controlled and the Contractor shall provide, install and maintain approved monitors for the detection of oxygen deficiency, and flammable and toxic gases at all times during the execution of the Works. These shall be located at working faces, at the bottom of shafts in excess of 8 m in depth, and at other locations as required having due regard to circumstances and the location, nature and type of work being undertaken.

1303. Lighting

1.   Lighting intensities shall not be less than 10 lux along the tunnel and 30 lux over a distance of ten times the width of tunnel or shaft from any junction or from portals or shaft connections.

1304. Noise Control

1.   Noise control shall be in accordance with BS 5228 Parts 1, 2 and 4.

1305. Blasting

1.   Blasting shall be in accordance with Clause 205.

2.   Electric cables shall be removed 50 m from any face where charging with explosives is in progress and any necessary temporary illumination shall be of an approved sealed type. Relaxation of this safety distance of 50 m may be approved provided the Contractor can justify such a relaxation by utilising appropriate blasting equipment and components.

1306. Communication

1.   Adequate means of communication shall be provided between the surface and the works below ground.

1307. Electrical Wiring

1. Wiring from the supply line for electric lights and power shall be properly installed and maintained and securely fastened in place. Separate circuits shall be provided for lighting and power purposes. As far as is practicable all light and power wires shall be kept clear of, and be placed on opposite sides of tunnels to, telephone and signal wires and wires used for firing blasts. All cabling shall be adequately protected against damage. All electrical equipment shall be adequately earthed. The voltage for all lighting and hand held power tools shall not exceed 110 volts and power shall be supplied from a transformer which has its centre point connected to earth.

1308. Setting Out

1. A surface network of precisely co-ordinated and levelled setting out stations of approved design shall be provided and sited outside the zone of influence of the Works. The co-ordinates and levels of these stations shall be made available to the Engineer for checking and approval.

1309. Tolerances

1. The position of the internal face of any pipeline, shaft or tunnel shall not deviate from that required by the Contract by more than the permissible deviations shown in Table 1300A.

TABLE 1300A

Work Category	Dimension or Alignment	Permissible Deviation
Pipeline	Level	12 mm
	Line	25 mm
Pipe jacking	Line	75 mm
	Level	50 mm
Shafts and Chambers	Vertically	1 in 300
Shafts and Tunnels	Finished diameter	1%
Tunnels without secondary lining	Line (shield drive)	75 mm
	Line (hand drive)	50 mm
	Level (shield drive)	50 mm
	Level (hand drive)	25 mm
Tunnels with secondary lining	Line	20 mm
	Level	10 mm
Shafts and Tunnel Segments	Maximum lipping between edges of adjacent segments	5 mm

1310. Subsidence

1. In the event of subsidence of the surface occurring on or adjacent to the line of a tunnel or in the vicinity of shafts during the progress of the Works or during the period of maintenance, the Contractor shall reinstate the surface to its original state and to the satisfaction of the Engineer.

2. Regular monitoring for subsidence, within the zone of influence of the Works, shall be carried out during the course of the Works and the period of maintenance and an interpretation of the results shall be provided to the Engineer.

1311. Headings

1. Headings are defined as small tunnels and shall comply with the relevant tunnel specification clauses.

2. Headings shall be supported to the extent necessary to prevent movement of surrounding ground and the ground surface, and to allow the work of pipelaying, jointing and surrounding of

the pipes and packing of the heading to proceed as *required by the Contract*. Unless otherwise directed the supports shall be withdrawn as the work of packing the heading proceeds.

3.   Headings which are to contain pipes shall be of the minimum size which will allow the pipes to be properly laid and surrounded with concrete or other material and the heading to be packed as *required by the Contract*.

4.   Where support frames are left in place they may, if approved, be allowed to encroach on the minimum thickness *required by the Contract* provided that (a) at no point there is less than 250 mm of concrete between the outside of the pipe and the side of the support frame; (b) dimensions of such frames measured along the axis of the pipe are not greater than 300 mm; and (c) such frames do not occur closer than 1 m centre to centre.

1312.   Tunnelling under Structures

1..   When tunnelling under or near structures the working face shall not be left unattended at any time and continuous shift working shall be adopted until such time as, in the opinion of the Engineer, the likelihood of damage occurring to structures is eliminated. At all such times, precautions shall be taken to minimise overbreak and, if necessary, the working face shall be held stable by immediate advancement of supports after excavation.

1313.   Excavation, General

1.   Spoil storage compounds of sufficient capacity to store the total calculated quantities of excavated material shall be provided.

2.   Shafts, other than those *required by the Contract*, shall be constructed only with the approval of the Engineer.

3.   The size of access or construction shafts, other than segmentally lined manholes, shall be large enough to allow the proper construction of an internally built manhole.

4.   The backfilling of all shafts shall be carried out as in accordance with Clause 214 or, if *required by the Contract*, shall be backfilled with concrete.

5.   After 48 hours notice that areas will be required for inspection and checking, the Contractor shall ensure that the Engineer has access to tunnels or shafts, without hindrance, to carry out such inspection and checking.

6.   All shafts shall be fitted with substantial and approved temporary access ladders with landings at intervals not exceeding 6 m. Protection shall be provided so that persons using the ladders are not subject to danger such as by the passage of skips or materials in the shafts.

7.   The tops of all shafts shall be made secure at all times by means of suitable barricades and have effective lighting and watching during all operations. Where the shafts are in public or private streets, the Contractor shall observe any precautions considered necessary by the Highway Authority, Police or the Engineer.

8.   Voids caused by slips, falls of material and overbreak during the excavating operations in tunnels and shafts shall be filled with concrete. As far as it is practicable this shall be done simultaneously with the concreting of the linings. Where this is not practicable, and behind steel arch ribs, bank bars and primary linings, the cavities shall be filled in advance with concrete grade C15 to such extent as will leave a thickness of lining to follow of not less than that required by the Contract. Such filling shall be shuttered to the satisfaction of the Engineer.

1314.   Excavation in Soft Material

1.   Excavation shall extend to the net size required to accommodate the lining rings.

2.   Immediately on excavating in soft material for a depth of one ring in shaft or tunnel, the Contractor shall erect segmental rings and shall secure these with bolts and grommets, and shall grout behind the rings as specified in Clause 1325. The Contractor shall take all necessary precautions to avoid loss of ground, ingress of water and all other conditions which might cause uneven loadings or settlements of the segmental rings, or otherwise impair the proper construction of the Works.

3.   In soft material or permeable strata the Contractor shall take such steps as are necessary to prevent the inflow of both water and material into the excavations.

4.   Tunnels to be constructed in soft material shall be excavated by shield or rotary drive.

1315. Excavation in Rock
1.   Care shall be exercised when blasting in the vicinity or suspected vicinity of a rock/soft interface, into and through igneous intrusions and wherever other excavations are in close proximity.

1316. Interfaces between Rock and Soft
1.   Where required and in particular, at any junction between rock and soft material in tunnels the Contractor shall probe ahead by drilling not less than four 32 mm diameter holes 15 m in advance of the working face and shall repeat the operation as required. The position and angling of the probes shall be as approved and, in general, two probes will be required near the top of the face and two on either side at shoulders, all angled to pass outside the proposed excavation line at 8 m from the face. Where necesary, grout shall be injected to stop the inflow of water.

1317. Tunnel Support and Protection, General
1.   Where it is necessary to support exposed areas supports shall be provided to the surrounding ground in tunnels and shafts to control and prevent any movement of the tunnel or ground surface.

2.   After blasting the Contractor shall carefully inspect the newly exposed rock faces and shall sound the rock, scale and support as necessary to ensure safe working conditions. The inspection shall extend back from the area of blasting and shall cover those areas likely to be affected by the particular blasts.

3.   Where soil stabilisation or working in compressed air becomes necessary to ensure proper safety of personnel and the effective completion of Permanent Works, the Contractor may immediately take the required steps and shall report these to the Engineer so that written approval of the final measures to be adopted may be given.

4.   Supports shall not be withdrawn without approval. Should it be necessary to withdraw support this shall be carried out as the work of permanent packing proceeds.

1318. Steel Arch Support
1.   Steel arch ribs and bank bars erected for support shall be firmly wedged in position and packed with concrete or grouted bags of the grade *required by the Contract*, so as to resist efficiently any tendency to movement of the rock at any point on the roof or sides of the tunnel. The bases of all arch ribs shall bear directly on to solid rock, or shall be underpinned with concrete on to solid rock. Before placing concrete lining, the position of any rib encroaching within 75 mm of the internal face shall be corrected.

1319. Rock Bolting and Dowelling
1.   Steel rock bolts or dowels shall be secured only within holes drilled into the roof and sides of rock excavations.

2.   After anchoring in the drill hole, the rock bolt shall be tensioned and the results reported to the Engineer for his approval.

3.   Prior to any rock bolting and dowelling being undertaken, the Contractor shall demonstrate, by means of trials, his proposed methods for inserting and stressing the rock bolts and dowels.

4.   All rock bolts and, or dowels shall be installed as immediate inline support unless otherwise approved.

1320. Bolted Precast Concrete Segmental Linings

1.   Precast concrete segments for tunnel lining shall be of the flanged and bolted type.

2.   Segmental joints to bolted concrete tunnel and shaft linings shall be trued and longitudinal joint bolts tightened before the final tightening of the circumferential joint bolts.

3.   Bituminous jointing strip shall be provided to longitudinal joints.

4.   Packings shall be inserted in the joints of the lining at the time of erection to maintain correct shape, line and level.

5.   Two grommets shall be threaded on each bolt at the time any bolted segment is erected. One grommet shall be placed under the washer at the head of the bolt and the other under the washer at the nut.

1321. Unbolted Precast Concrete Tunnel Segments

1.   The shape of unbolted concrete segmental tunnels shall be maintained with tolerance after erection, until segments have been stabilised by grout or other means.

2.   Where a circumferential prestress is necessary for erection the force shall be such that the whole of the concrete lining is expanded tight against the surrounding ground. An approved graphite compound shall be applied to the wedge faces of segments immediately prior to expanding the ring.

3.   Where wedge block segments are specified or approved, the excavated tunnel periphery shall be lubricated to reduce skin friction.

4.   Where key segments are shorter than other segments comprising the ring, the pockets formed shall be filled with concrete grade C35.

1322. Caulking of Joints

1.   All joints shall be thoroughly caulked, with approved material, after raking and cleaning out. Joints which are not watertight shall be recaulked as necessary.

1323. Granolithic Lining to Segmental Rings

1.   Before construction of the internal lining of the segmental rings the tunnel shall be cleaned out.

2.   Unless otherwise *required by the Contract* or directed granolithic lining shall be 100 mm thick over the ribs of the segments. The surface finish shall be as *required by the Contract*.

3.   The shuttering system to be used shall be approved and shall be thoroughly cleaned and oiled after each use. It should be sufficiently supported so as not to allow any deflection under loading.

4.   Granolithic concrete to shaft and tunnel linings shall consist of one part cement, one part sand, one part crushed granite aggregate from 10 mm downwards and two parts 12 mm whinstone.

1324. In Situ Concrete Linings

1.   Before concreting, all rock surfaces to be in contact with the in situ concrete lining shall be thoroughly cleaned and scaled of all loose or defective rock, and thoroughly washed down with a water jet under not less than 140 kN/m^2 pressure.

2.   Surfaces of primary linings shall be thoroughly cleaned and washed down before concreting takes place.

3.   All formwork shall be true to form, securely made and supported, and all suspension arrangements shall be designed to operate in a safe and secure manner to ensure the safety of the persons and the Works at all times. Adequate precautions shall be taken to prevent risk from dropping of materials, and all formwork shall be inspected before any concreting is commenced.

4.   The face of the formwork shall be approved before concreting. Access panels shall be provided in the units to facilitate the placing, vibration and consolidation of the concrete.

5.   Concrete shall be placed continuously in each length of formwork.

6.   Care shall be taken in the case of exposed concrete faces of the tunnel and shaft linings that no irregularity or roughness remains between the successive sections of the formwork and the finished concrete face must be as *required in the Contract*.

7.   The build up of water pressure behind linings which are being cast or which are immature, shall be prevented.

8.   The sequence of work within the tunnels or shafts shall be so arranged that no damage or adverse effects, shall occur to permanent linings. The proposed sequences and methods of operations shall be submitted to the Engineer sufficiently in advance of commencement of the Works, for his consideration and approval.

1325.   Grouting, General
1.   Grouting shall commence at holes nearest to the tunnel invert, and grouting of each hole shall continue until there is no further take of grout at the specified pressure. When grouting through each hole has been completed the valve shall be left in position until the grout has had time to set after which the appropriate plugs shall be inserted.

2.   Grouting shall be carried out by pressure pumps and not by air pressure. Pumps shall be capable of producing pressures up to 4 bar in excess of the air pressure in the shafts or tunnels.

1326.   Cavity Grouting
1.   The type of equipment used, the order in which the holes are drilled and grouted, the composition of the mixture and the pressures to be used shall be as *required by the Contract*.

2.   Accurate records shall be kept showing the number, location and depth of all holes, the quantity of grout taken by each and the pressures used.

3.   Grouting into cavities shall be carried out as follows:-
   (a)   Between in situ concrete linings and rock by drilling through the lining, inserting grouting tubes in the holes and injecting grout at a pressure as *required by the Contract*.

   (b)   Between mass concrete backing to primary linings or steel arch supports and rock by drilling through the mass concrete backing, at the grout holes in the case of primary linings, inserting grout tubes in the holes and injecting grout at a pressure as *required by the Contract*. Grouting shall be carried out after erection of not more than 15m of linings or supports.

   (c)   Between primary linings and material other than rock, ring by ring in shaft work and after not more than three rings in tunnel work by blocking off between the surrounding strata and the leading edge of the ring and injecting grout through the grout holes until the ring is solidly embedded.

4.   In permeable strata, to limit the spread and take of grout, an approved accelerator shall be added to the grout mix. Grouting shall take place in a series of repeated small injections to form

an effective seal adjacent to the primary lining. All materials and procedures for this shall be as *required by the Contract*.

5.   Cavity grouting shall normally be carried out by pressure pumps but equipment using air pressure may be employed, if approved.

6.   Where primary linings are not used grouting shall not be carried out before the in situ lining achieves the specified 28 day characteristic strength.

1327.   Grouting of Rock Fissures

1.   If required, grouting of fissures in rock shall be carried out in local areas of tunnels and shafts to control the ingress of water where:-

(a)   it would impair the effective placing of the in situ lining, or

(b)   it would affect the integrity of the tunnel or shaft, or

(c)   the quantity involved could not be dealt with normally.

2.   If required grouting of fissures in rock shall be carried out over the whole or part of the length of rock tunnel to seal off any nascent fissures or weakened bedding planes induced in the rock by tunnel driving. This grouting shall take place after placing of in situ lining and cavity grouting or after erection of primary linings, placing of backing concrete and cavity grouting.

3.   Grouting of rock fissures shall normally be a single stage operation, but where directed grout holes shall be redrilled and flushed out and second stage grouting shall be carried out.

4.   Grout mixtures, pressures, spacing and penetration of holes, shall be as *required by the Contract*.

1328.   Work in Compressed Air

1.   Compressed air working in any portion of the Works shall have prior approval in writing and only if the Contractor can demonstrate that it is either unsafe or impracticable to construct the work satisfactorily in free air.

2.   The Contractor shall reserve adequate space in his working areas to accommodate all equipment and protective enclosures which are necessary for compressed air working. He shall submit for approval drawings of his working areas showing the location of all such equipment.

3.   Details of proposed bulkheads and air locks shall be submitted for approval.

4.   The Contractor's programme and schedule of resources shall include full details of the capacity and type of compressed air plant.

5.   All plant and equipment shall be maintained at constant readiness.

6.   Decompression stages and times shall be in accordance with CIRIA Report No. 44.

7.   The compressed air shall be varied to suit external hydrostatic pressure and shall not exceed the minimum required to permit the work to proceed in safety.

8.   At each location where compressed air is used instruments shall be provided to give a continuous indication of the pressure within the workings and the atmospheric pressure. The Engineer shall have access to these at all times.

9.   Air pressure at the main receivers and in working chambers of caissons, tunnels and shaft shall be recorded at approved intervals and entered in a register. A duplicate copy shall be given each day to the Engineer.

10.   When directed the Contractor shall release the compressed air from the workings to allow the Engineer to ascertain that the new construction is watertight.

1329. Control of Water

1.   Adequate temporary drains and sumps shall be provided in the inverts of tunnels to ensure that the works can be maintained in a dry condition. When no longer required temporary drains shall be grouted or filled with concrete.

1330. Pipe Jacking

1.   In shafts to be used for pipe jacking thrust supports shall be provided to ensure that the shaft lining is not damaged.

2.   The Contractor shall submit a method statement before commencement of the works.

3.   Pipe jacking once commenced shall be carried out in one continuous operation.

4.   Pipe jacking shall be carried out in accordance with the tolerances given in Table 1300A.

5.   Excavation for pipe jacking shall be undertaken from within a shield equipped with steering jacks for adjusting the alignment. Face boards shall be available for boarding up the exposed excavation.

6.   Intermediate jacking stations may be used to limit jacking forces.

7.   The thrust load shall be imparted to the pipes through a suitable thrust ring to ensure even distribution of the load. Resilient packing material shall be used between the pipe end and the thrust ring.

8.   The pipe manufacturer's stated permitted draw or angular deflection shall not be exceeded at joints.

9.   The Contractor shall maintain site records of thrusting pressures and line and level measurements.

10.   All lifting and grouting holes shall be sealed with approved mortar.

11.   Cavities behind jacked sleeves shall be filled with grout injected under pressure through holes bored in the sleeve. The number of holes required to prove the adequacy of the grouting operation shall be as approved.

12.   After completion of jacking any minor leaks at pipe joints shall be sealed by caulking or other approved methods.

Reconditioning of Mains

1401. Definitions

1. The Contractor will be given possession of the main in the sequence *required by the Contract* unless otherwise directed.

2. The Contractor shall provide such means as may be necessary for removing any water remaining in the pipe when he takes possession and shall be responsible for dealing with water passing either line or branch valves.

3. Where man access to the pipes is *required by the Contract*, the Contractor shall provide all equipment necessary to ensure the safety of persons authorised to enter the pipe.

1402. Cleaning

1. All rust, tuberculation, deposits, loose or deteriorated remains of original coating and other foreign matter shall be removed from the inside of the pipe by an approved method.

2. The Contractor shall determine the availability, location and suitability of any water supply which he may require for his operations. He shall make his own arrangements for the transportation of water to the site.

3. All water and residual debris from the cleaning process shall be removed from the site by the Contractor.

4. Unless *required by the Contract*, or otherwise approved the Contractor shall not scrape through the existing in-line valves.

1403. Fettling of Joints

1. On man access mains fettling of joints shall be carried out after scraping and prior to inspection. Joints shall be cleaned out and filled with cement mortar flush with the inside of the main.

1404. Inspection of Pipeline prior to Lining

1. After cleaning, the pipeline will be inspected by the Engineer and any defects or infiltration shall be repaired as *required by the Contract* prior to the lining being applied.

1405. Connections to Pipeline

1. During cleaning and lining of the main, blockages shall not be allowed to occur in service pipes, branches, air valves, scours or fire hydrants connected to the main.

2. All connections shall be checked by the Contractor to ensure that they are in working order after completion of the lining and before inspection by the Engineer.

1406. Cement Mortar for Lining

1. Cement mortar for lining shall consist of 1 to 1.5 parts sand to 1 part of cement by weight. The maximum water cement ratio shall be:-

TABLE 1400A

Pipe Diameter	Water Cement Ratio
Less than 150 mm	0.45
150 to 650 mm	0.40
Greater than 650 mm	0.35

2.   The mortar mix shall be designed by the Contractor to achieve the required lining thickness and surface finish. Mortar shall be prepared in a paddle type mixer.

3.   The cement mortar lining shall not be applied when the air temperature is less than -1 °C on a rising thermometer, and less than 1 °C on a falling thermometer.

1407.   Thickness of Cement Mortar Lining
1.   The thickness of mortar lining, which must be obtained in one pass through the main, shall comply with Table 1400B.

TABLE 1400B

Pipe Diameter mm	Type of Finish	Lining Thickness mm	Tolerance mm
Less than 150	Untrowelled 'Orange Peel'	6	+2, ϕ
150 to 450	Trowel	6	+2, −0
450 and above	Trowel	10	+2, −0

1408.   Lining
1.   The cement mortar lining shall be applied continuously in the lengths as shown in Table 1400C or as *required by the Contract*.

TABLE 1400C

Diameter Range m	Access Hole Frequency m	
	min	max
75 to 150	100	150
175 to 300	100	180
325 to 650	130	230
675 to 1200	150	500*
1200	150	600*

* Lining carried out from both access holes

2.   In mains of less than 150mm diameter an untrowelled, 'Orange Peel' finish is acceptable. Surface indentations shall not exceed 1.5 mm.

3.   In mains ranging between 150 and 500 mm diameter the surface finish shall be achieved by using a drag trowel.

4.   For mains greater than 500 mm diameter the surface finish shall be achieved by using a drag trowel or rotating trowels.

5.   On completion of machine lining hand trowelling of any minor defects over small areas or joints shall not be carried out without approval.

6.   The lining of the pipe shall terminate at the first joint of any branch.

7.   After completion and approval of the lining of each section of the main between line valves a period of 10 hours shall elapse before refilling and testing.

1409. Testing of Mains

1.   The Contractor shall test the main to its maximum working pressure in sections as the work progresses. Each section shall be terminated by a valve, blank flange or cap as *required by the Contract*. The Contractor shall open and shut valves as directed.

1410. Inspection of Small Diameter Mains

1.   Where man access is not possible mains shall be inspected after cleaning and again after lining by means of a fibrescope, CCTV or a combination of both as *required by the Contract*. The Contractor shall provide and retain the equipment on site as *required by the Contract*.

1411. Disinfection

1.   Disinfection and flushing out shall be as *required by the Contract*.

Sewer Renovation

1501. Atmosphere Monitoring

1. When any person is in a confined space the atmosphere at the workplace and at the base of all access shafts shall be continuously monitored to detect oxygen deficiency, flammable and toxic gases. The Contractor shall maintain and calibrate the monitoring equipment in accordance with the manufacturer's instructions.

1502. Lighting

1. Where lighting is required it shall comply with BS 6164.

1503. Lining Design

1. The lining shall be designed in accordance with the procedures given in the WAA/WRc Sewerage Rehabilitation Manual.

1504. Sewer Flows

1. Working areas shall be kept free of flows unless otherwise approved. If the sewer flows exceed the Contractor's agreed diversionary provisions the sewer shall be immediately evacuated.

1505. Preparation General

1. All debris removed from sewers shall be removed from site to an approved tip to be found by the Contractor.

2. The Contractor shall take all precautions necessary to prevent debris being carried downstream of the working area.

1506. Repair of Man Entry Sewers

1. Repairs to lengths of man entry sewer shall be carried out in such a manner, and over such area at any one time that the stability of the existing sewer is not jeopardised.

1507. Cleaning of Surfaces

1. All deposits which are likely to jeopardise the performance of the lining shall be removed. Cleaning shall be carried out only by approved methods.

1508. Inspection

1. Relining work shall not be permitted until the prepared sewer has been inspected and approved by the Engineer.

1509. Proving of Man Entry Systems

1. Immediately prior to installation a template of sufficient rigidity and length to represent the proposed lining system shall be passed down the length to be relined to confirm the minimum size of annulus.

2. A sample of sewer lining unit shall be used to ensure that access for the lining can be gained to all sections of the sewer to be renovated.

1510. Proving of Non Entry Systems Excluding ''Insituform''

1. Immediately prior to installation a proving pig with solid ends and of sufficient rigidity and length to represent the proposed lining system shall be passed down the length to be relined.

1511.   Line and Level Tolerance
1.   The position of the internal face of any unit shall not deviate from that *required in the Contract* by more than:-

> Permissible Deviations
> Line ± 25 mm;
> Level ± 12 mm.

2.   In man entry sewers, each lining unit shall be positioned so as to maintain at least the minimum specified annulus. Maximum lipping between adjacent lining units shall be 5 mm.

3.   The lining shall be packed off the existing sewer by means of wedges of lining material, hardwood or other approved material.

4.   Lining shall not have a backfall unless otherwise approved.

1512.   "Insituform" Installation
1.   The lining shall be transported to site according to the manufacturer's instructions.

2.   The Contractor shall have regard to weather conditions in deciding when to transport the impregnated lining to the site and when to commence insertion.

3.   For sewers with running infiltration, a prelining shall be installed prior to lining inversion to prevent the uncured resin from being washed out of the lining bag.

4.   The lining shall be inverted from upstream to downstream into the prepared sewer using cold water.

5.   The Contractor shall ensure that the pressure in the lining exceeds both the pressure due to the groundwater head given by the Engineer in the lining design sheet and any pressure due to sewage in laterals.

1513.   "Insituform" Curing
1.   As soon as the lining has been fully inverted, the resin shall be cured by raising, maintaining and then lowering the internal water temperature in a predetermined manner to suit the resin system used. The rate of temperature rise and fall during heating and cooling shall not exceed 1°C per minute. The curing water shall not be released until it reaches a temperature below 40°C.

1514.   "Insituform" Quality Control Tests
1.   Quality control tests shall be carried out by the Contractor on each lining length after it has been installed and cured. The sample procurement and test methods given in Water Authorities Association Information and Guidance Note No. 4-34-04 shall be used.

1515.   Sliplining
1.   Details of the proposed method of winching must be submitted to the Engineer for approval at least 7 days before the insertion date.

2.   The winch shall be fitted with a direct reading load gauge to measure the winching load. At the end of each day's winching the Contractor shall provide the Engineer with copies of the forces recorded in winching at the start of any pull and during the pull at increments of 20 m of winching distance and at any restart after temporary stops.

3. The Contractor shall supply sufficient cable in one continuous length so that the pull may be continuous between approved winching points.

4. The winch, cable and cable drum shall be provided with a safety cage and supports so that it may be operated safely without injury to persons or property.

5. The Contractor shall provide a system of guide pulleys and bracings at each intermediate manhole to minimise cable contact with the existing sewer between manholes.

6. A nose cone shall be fixed to the first pipe to be inserted and shall be fitted with a swivel attachment to reduce the twist transmission between the winch cable and the nose cone.

7. Lubricant to ease the pull shall be used only if approved and shall be water or bentonite.

8. Supports to trench sheets shall remain completely separate from the pipe support system and shall be so designed that neither the pipe nor the winch cable shall be in contact with them.

9. Polyethylene pipes shall be supported by a system of rollers at intervals of less than 4 m.

10. Rollers shall be firmly anchored and, where required capable of vertical and horizontal adjustment.

1516. Jointing
1. Joints between lining units shall be made and secured in accordance with the manufacturer's instructions. Contact surfaces shall be cleaned immediately prior to jointing.

1517. Jointing of Precast Gunite Segments
1. Joints between precast gunite segments shall be made with in situ gunite. Joint surfaces shall have all laitance and loose material removed and be thoroughly cleaned and wetted before in situ gunite is sprayed. Areas of the work which exhibit a lack of compaction or bond, dry patches, voids, sand pockets or sagged or slumped materials shall be removed and resprayed immediately.

2. The Contractor shall take precautions to ensure that air pockets will not be trapped during subsequent grouting.

1518. Jointing by Polyethylene Butt Fusion Welding
1. Polyethylene pipes shall be capable of jointing by fusion welding techniques and be jointed in accordance with Clause 511.

1519. Cutting of Linings
1. Linings shall be cut using approved methods. Precautions shall be taken to avoid delamination or spalling. Cut edges of glass reinforced plastic pipes shall be adequately sealed with a suitable compatible resin.

1520. Treatment at End of Lining
1. At the upstream end of the lining the existing invert shall be broken out and the lining laid on a class M5 mortar bed so that inverts are level. At all other points the existing sewer shall be suitably prepared and a smooth transition made with class M5 mortar.

2. At intermediate manholes the lining soffit shall be removed. The edges shall be sealed and the benching made good with a mortar compatible with the chemical resistance of the lining material.

1521. Treatment at Ends and Edges of Polyethylene and Polypropylene Linings
1.   All exposed edges and ends of polyethylene and polypropylene linings shall be mechanically anchored using suitable fixings.

1522. Laterals
1.   All laterals shall be reconnected by an approved method except those which the Engineer specifically designates as abandoned. Connections shall not be made at or within 100 mm of a circumferential lining joint.

2.   The finished connection shall be made flush with the lined sewer and shall provide a smooth transition to the existing lateral pipework.

1523. Reconnection of Laterals to PE Sliplining
1.   At least 24 hours shall be allowed between the completion of a sliplining pull and the reconnection of laterals to allow the lining to relax.

1524. Grouting Plant
1.   Grout shall be mixed in a paddle, high shear or colloidal grout mixer. Grout hoses shall be at least 38 mm internal diameter.

2.   Grout plant shall be chosen with regard to the relationship between its output, the length and volume of annulus and the grout setting time. The grout shall be sieved before being pumped. The grouting nozzle shall not project beyond the lining into the annulus by more than 5mm.

1525. Annulus Grouting
1.   Adequate venting shall be provided and vent holes shall be plugged when all air, water and contaminated or watery grout has been released. A minimum of two air vents shall be provided. The pressure shall be continuously measured by a suitable gauge fitted at the injection nozzle. The injection pressure shall not exceed 50 kN/m^2. The gauge shall have a full scale reading of not more than 200 kN/m^2.

2.   The Contractor shall provide calibration certificates for all gauges used. If directed the Contractor shall have gauges retested by an approved firm and new test certificates provided.

3.   Means of immediate communication between nozzle operator and pump operator shall be maintained during grouting and a means of rapidly stopping the grout flow shall be provided.

4.   At each injection point the quantity of grout injected and the maximum pressure at the nozzle shall be recorded and the records made available to the Engineer.

5.   All equipment and hoses shall be thoroughly cleaned after each use.

6.   The distance the grout is to travel, whether in hose or in annulus, shall not exceed 100 m.

7.   The dry constituents shall be thoroughly mixed with water to achieve the specified water to solids ratio. Grout shall be used within 1 hour of mixing.

8.   Unacceptable or surplus grout shall not be disposed of into any sewer or watercourse.

1526. Continuous Grouting of Non Man Entry Sewers
1.   Where continuous grouting is required the Contractor shall take all necessary precautions to ensure that any delay due to blockage or mechanical breakdown is minimised and will not affect the performance of the placed grout.

Sewer Renovation   **Clause 1527.1 — 1529.1**

1527. Grout Injection

1. Man Entry

Grout shall be injected through a minimum of three holes per 5 m length of lining located in the haunches and crown of the lining section. Grouting shall proceed from downstream to upstream from the lowest grout holes to the highest.

2. Non Man Entry

The maximum distance between grout injection points shall be 50 m. Grout shall be injected from the downstream end of the renovated sewer.

1528. Grout Tests

1. Where tests are required for different properties, the tests shall be carried out on samples from the same batch.

2. The density and workability of every batch shall be determined.

3. The density shall not differ by more than 5% from the type test result.

4. The workability results shall not differ by more than 125 mm or 5 seconds, Trough or Cone test respectively, from the type test result.

5. The Contractor shall make 3 grout cubes as detailed below from samples taken from every 5 m^3 of grout or 50 m of grouted annulus, whichever is the smaller.

6. Cubes shall be prepared, cured and tested as the type test. The results shall be not less than the type test requirement for the cube strength *required by the Contract*.

1529. Cleaning after Grouting

1. Immediately after each grouting operation the Contractor shall clean out any excess grout from the sewer and laterals.

138

APPENDICES

These appendices do not form part of the specification

APPENDIX I
DETAILS OF PROBLEM/COMPLAINT UPON QUALITY ASSURED PRODUCTS

1. Name of complainant _____

2. The product and specification reference _____

_____

3. Name of manufacturer _____

4. Details of the product i.e. size, type, class, date of manufacture (if known), batch number (if known) etc.

_____

_____

_____

5. How many items appear unsatisfactory? _____

6. How many items were ordered? _____

7. Were quality assured products ordered?   YES/NO

8. Were all the products delivered, marked with a mark of conformity?   YES/NO

9. Date the products were delivered _____

10. When was the problem identified? _____

11. Were the products supplied by: the manufacturer/a merchant

12. With which clauses of the specification do the products appear not to comply:

Nos. _____

13 Details of problem/complaint _____

_____

_____

14. Has the manufacturer been advised of the problem?   YES/NO

15. If yes to 14 what was the response? _____

_____

16. If no to 14, do you wish us to reveal to the manufacturer that you are the complainant   YES/NO

17. Have the products all been installed?   YES/NO

18. Do you wish the products to be examined on Site by a certification body representative?   YES/NO

19. If yes to 18 please give details of Site location and name of contact
(We shall arrange a mutually convenient date to visit the site.)

GENERAL NOTES

Introduction
1.   These notes are intended for the guidance of Engineers on the use of the Specification and indicate, where appropriate, the reasons for the way in which the clauses were drafted. These notes do not form part of the specification.

Incorporation
2.   The Specification is complete in itself and can be used to cover a wide range of water and sewerage schemes. It is not necessary to reproduce the Specification in the Contract; it should be incorporated by reference.

Application of the Specification
3.   It is essential that the Specification be used in conjunction with a complete set of drawings. Requirements additional to the Specification should be covered by additional clauses. It is intended that the Specification be used intact but where amendments or additions are necessary, the following procedures should be adopted, care being taken to avoid matters which are covered in the Conditions of Contract.

   (a)   Substitute Clause or Sub-Clause
Where an alteration or addition to a printed clause or sub-clause is necessary, a substitute text should normally be written to replace the whole of the printed clause or sub-clause. As far as possible the original text should be re-worded sufficiently only to include the required additional information. It should be given the original title and number suffixed 'S'. However, if the alteration is slight and can be made by a simple ''delete and substitute'' instruction, such a method should be used.

   (b)   Additional Clause or Sub-Clause
Where an additional clause or sub-clause is required to supplement the Specification, it should be given the desired title and the number subsequent to the last one of the appropriate Series in the printed Specification.

Clauses containing phrases with special significance.
4.   Certain clauses contain phrases such as 'as required by the Contract' or 'unless otherwise provided in the Contract' which impose a requirement on the Engineer to ensure that the contract documents and drawings as a whole are explicit and adequately describe what is required. These phrases have been printed in italics in the Specification and a list of the relevant clauses is included as an Appendix to these Notes.

Tolerances
5.   It is not considered necessary or desirable to specify tolerances for all dimensions required in the Contract. Where dictated by functional or aesthetic need, some tolerances are included in the Specification. If the Engineer specially requires tolerances to apply these should be shown on the Drawings. Unnecessarily fine tolerances have the effect of elevating prices and should therefore be avoided.

Proprietary Materials
6.   Specifying a single proprietary article or material should be avoided as far as possible but in particular circumstanes where these are required in the Contract, the brand name or type should be followed by 'or equivalent'.

Supervision and Testing
7.   Adequate testing of materials and checking of workmanship standards is necessary to ensure compliance with the Specification which is based on the assumption that only competent Contractors will be employed and that Engineers have an adequate control and supervisory organisation.

Quality Control
8.   No mention is made in the Specification of quality control, as this is a method of recording compliance with the Specification, and does not affect the technical requirements. If it is required, appropriate additional clauses should be included.

British Standard Specifications and British Standard Codes of Practice

9.   Throughout the Specification dates of and amendments to British Standards or British Standard Codes of Practice are not quoted. Clause 112 makes it clear that the British Standards and British Standard Codes of Practice applicable to any Contract will be the latest editions published 42 days prior to the last date for submission of the Tender. In all cases, the equivalent European standard is acceptable.

Building Drainage

10.   British Standard Code of Practice CP8301 Building Drainage and BS 800 Part 14 Code of Practice for below ground drainage deal with the design and construction of both foul and surface water drains between buildings and the sewer connection may be more appropriate for drains serving buildings rather than the clauses in the Standard Specification.

SERIES 100 SITE CLEARANCE, ACCESS AND GENERAL

101.   Offices for the Engineer

1.   It is intended that the location of the offices should be decided by the Contractor subject to the approval of the Engineer. However, in certain circumstances the location may be shown in the Contract. In such cases, as the provision of services can be expensive, consideration should be given to the economical availability of existing telephone, water and electricity services at the selected site.

2.   The details of the testing equipment will vary with each Contract depending on the type of work.

4.   A list of the required surveying instruments should be shown in the contract. Because of the value of some instruments for example, microptic theodolite, consideration should be given to requiring provision of such only when necessary rather than requiring permanent availability on the Site of expensive instruments which will only be used occasionally.

105.   Privately Owned and Public Utility Services

2.   The route of existing Public Utility Services together with their dimensions as obtained from the various Undertakers should be shown on a combined drawing with drawing code and a provisional sum entered in the Bill of Quantitites to cover the precise location of any doubtful service line.

108.   Working Area

1.   When deciding the boundaries of the working area and accesses thereto in the Contract, it should not be forgotten that the extent of these areas will be affected by the size of the pipe and the depth of the trenches in the case of a pipeline Contract. Recommendations for suitable minimum working widths for pipe tracks are given in Table W. In the case of a Contract requiring the use of concreting plant the working area will require to allow for the mixing plant and the aggregate and reinforcement storage area.

TABLE W

Nominal Diameter of Pipe mm	Recommended minimum width of working area metres			
	Depth to Invert of Pipe			
	0-2m	2-3m	3-4m	4-6m
100-200	8	9	10	12
200-300	9	10	11	13
300-600	10	11	12	16
600-900	10	11	12	16
900-1200	11	12	13	19
1200-1500	12	14	16	22
1500-1800	13	16	19	25

4.   Nothwithstanding the provisions of Clause 19(1) of the Conditions of Contract there may be situations where it is in the Employer's interest that a temporary fence be erected, for example, to satisfy the landowner or tenant across whose ground a pipeline is being laid or to enable the part of a pasture not affected by the works to be grazed without fear of injury to the animals. To meet this situation items can be inserted in the Bill of Quantities whereby the Engineer could order the Contractor to erect temporary fences as specified in Clause 801 on the boundaries of the working area.

109.   Explosives
Detailed information on the handling and use of explosives is given in BS 5607: Code of practice for the safe use of explosives in the construction industry.

Additional Clauses

Noise Control
Where circumstances require the Contractor to avoid creating undue noise during particular periods of the day or night consideration should be given to including additional clauses defining these periods and the conditions which will apply.

Attention is drawn to the practices recommended in BS 5228: Code of practice for noise control on construction and demolition sites, and to the requirements of the Control of Pollution Act 1974, Part III (Noise), with particular reference to sections 60-61.

SERIES 200 EXCAVATION, BACKFILLING AND RESTORATION

201.   General
1.   Where any type of piling is necessary for the support of excavations, or as an integral part of the contract works, additional clauses in the specification and appropriate items in the Bill of Quantities will be required. The Institution of Civil Engineers publication ''Piling - Model Procedures and Specifications'' is recommended as a source of further information on the subject.

204.   Excavation in Rock
A definition of rock will be necessary in the Preamble to the Bill of Quantities. A suggested definition is as follows:-

8.   ''Rock shall mean''

(a)   the following geological deposits (to be listed by the Engineer) and
(b)   any hard material requiring the use of blasting or approved tools for its loosening before removal, or if excavated by hand, the use of wedges or sledgehammers.

Isolated volumes of such materials shall only be regarded as rock if so defined in the Civil Engineering Standard Method of Measurement, 2nd Edition, Class E, Measurement Rule M8.

206.   Preparation of Final Surface
2.   The provisions of this Clause in respect of the limitation of use of explosives requires provision of appropriate items in the Bill of Quantities.

Excavations
Attention is drawn to the requirement that the Clauses in this Series have, in respect of their reference to Pipe Trenches, to be read with the particular requirements which are set out in Clause 503, 505, 506 and 515 of the Specification, in respect of existing land drains and field drains or French drains set out in Clauses 516 and 517 respectively and in respect of their reference to Tunnelling and Pipe Jacking set out in Series 1300.

SERIES 300 MATERIALS

303. Aggregates for Concrete
4. Certain natural aggregates in Scotland, for example, dolerites and basalts, have high volume changes on wetting and drying so that high drying shrinkage occurs in concrete made with such aggregates. This can seriously impair the durability of exposed concrete, unless precautions are taken.

Information and recommendations on this matter are contained in the Building Research Establishment Digest No. 35 (Second Series) and the British Cement Association publication "Impurities in Concreting Aggregates" Ref. 45016.

Engineers may wish to specify that certain materials, such as aggregates, cement, ready-mixed concrete and reinforcing steel should be supplied in accordance with an accredited quality assurance scheme.

326. Gullies, Gully Gratings and Frames
5. If gullies of plastic materials are used in or alongside roadways other than access ways for light traffic, or in locations where ground loadings are high they must be surrounded by in-situ concrete at least 150 mm thick.

327. Handrails
2. Due to the wide variety of proprietary brands of handrail and of the various situations in which they may be used it is not practicable to produce a standard specification to cover all types.

342. Pipes, Fittings and Joints, and Bedding Material
1-16 Pipes supplied in accordance with this Specification are batch tested. 'Tested' pipes are individually tested and necessitate specific detailing in the Contract where required.

SERIES 400 FORMWORK AND CONCRETE

411. Types of Finish, Formed Surfaces
1. The term 'formed surfaces' refers to surfaces of concrete which require to be supported by formwork.

412. Types of Finish, Unformed Surfaces
1. The term 'unformed surfaces' refers to surfaces of concrete which do not require to be supported by formwork.

420. Designed Mixes
3. In specifying the requirements for a Designed Mix, the essential information that must be given is:

    (a)   The grade
    (b)   The permitted type(s) of cement
    (c)   The permitted type(s) of aggregate
    (d)   The nominal maximum size of aggregates
    (e)   The maximum and minimum cement contents
    (f)   The rate of sampling to be adopted for strength testing
    (g)   The acceptable limits of aggregate drying shrinkage
    (h)   Any special requirements.

439. Granolithic Concrete
10. Clause 438 is intended for general use. A mix suitable for use in tunnels in specified in Clause 1323.

446. Testing of Liquid Retaining Structures

2. The stabilising period of 7 days after filling is based upon a maximum design crack width of 0.1 mm. The stabilising period may need to be increased to 21 days for a maximum design crack width of 0.2 mm or greater.

448. Sterilisation of Structures

1. The specified strength of solution (50 mg per litre) will be adequate for general use and at the same time will be comparatively safe in use although care will still be necessary. In particular circumstances, however, and depending on the method of application and the type and size of the structure, higher strength solutions may be required. The Engineer should consider all the relevant factors before deciding which strength to adopt. The need for stringent safety precautions when working with high strength solutions is emphasised.

SERIES 500 PIPELAYING AND JOINTING

General

The Specification has been prepared generally in accordance with the principles set out in BS 8301 and BS 8005 although bedding factors for example might be selected from WAA Information and Guidance Note: 4-11-02.

It should be noted that clauses on Tolerances, Testing of Sewers, Pressure Pipelines and Bedding Material, Swabbing, Scouring and Sterilisation of Mains have been included in this Series.

501. Pipelines, General

1. Not all manufacturers make pipes which can be jointed with those from another manufacturer.

503. Excavation of Pipelines

2. In areas of high amenity it may be necessary to direct the removal of turf and topsoil from the whole of the working area and appropriate means of payment should be provided for in the Bill of Quantities.

The trench widths quoted in the Specification were determined from the dimensions necessary to place and compact bedding material with an allowance for sheeting. Where the depth of trench is shallower than the 'transition depth' the specified trench width may be exceeded. Where due to special circumstances trenches are to have widths greater than those specified the pipe and bedding strengths should be checked and the Specification amended if necessary.

Where the design conditions are changed, for example by the Contractor electing to use a larger diameter pipe, by excess width of trench, or by change in depth of trench, designs of the required strengths should be prepared.

505. Withdrawal of Supports

The greatest care is required when withdrawing trench supports to ensure that compacted bedding material is not disturbed and that voids left by the supports are properly filled and compacted. Where the ground permits, the supports should be withdrawn just clear of the area to take granular material before it is placed, but in very poor conditions it might be necessary to support the bottom section of the trench separately from the top section and to leave the supports at the bottom in place after backfilling.

506. Bedding and Protecting Pipes

A distinction is to be made between the requirements of bedding, haunching and surrounding and those of backfilling. The former comprises all operations of this kind up to a level 300mm above the top of the barrel of the pipe. Backfilling constitutes the remaining operations up to ground level or to the underside of any surface which is to be reinstated.

Appendix III illustrates standard pipe bedding arrangements but many other alternatives are possible.

In certain ground conditions the construction of a pipeline with granular bedding might give rise to undesirable movements of ground water and in these circumstances dams should be constructed at intervals across the trenches.

Where testing of the pipes requires that the joints be exposed, sufficient of the haunching and surround material should be placed to anchor the pipes against testing forces.

507. Plugs
Where trenches are liable to flood, sufficient haunching, surrounding and backfilling material should be placed to prevent flotation when the pipe ends are sealed.

514 Cutting Pipes
Attention is drawn to the precautions necessary when cutting asbestos materials and reference should be made to WAA Information and Guidance Note: 4-12-03 particularly with regard to Health and Safety.

SERIES 600 MANHOLES AND CHAMBERS

General
The type drawings included here are intended to illustrate basic manholes and to accord with BS 8005. They are intended to give guidance in the preparation of contract drawings in order to achieve a measure of uniformity.

The drawings cover brickwork manholes up to 3.5 m deep and precast concrete manholes up to 4.5 m deep for pipelines up to 600 mm diameter. It is intended that manholes outwith these parameters should be given specific consideration.

Modifications to the Specification may be required, for example, as follows:-

1. Manhole structures

   (i) Brick walls may require, in certain circumstances, to be thicker than indicated.

   (ii) The distance from the outer face of the wall to the first pipe joint outside the manhole should not exceed 500 mm or the diameter of the pipe, whichever is the greater.

2. Ground Water

Hydraulically, where ground water conditions require:-

   (i) The joints between segments of concrete manhole can be improved by the application of an external coat of cold applied joint sealing compound or by protective tape or by a combination of these.

   (ii) The cement or mortar backing to step irons which project through segments of concrete manholes can be made more watertight with one or more coats of the above compound.

   (iii) Backfill may require to be selected clay material thoroughly consolidated to form a barrier to the passage of ground water along granular material supporting the pipe.

SERIES 700 BUILDERWORK

General Note
This Series is intended for use only with minor building works of a nature similar to domestic house construction. Where it is proposed to use proprietary types of building systems additional clauses will require to be drafted for inclusion in the Specification.

703. Jointing and Pointing
Recommendations on the selection of mortars for use in particular circumstances is given in BS 5628.

704. Damp Proof Course
1. Where tanking of a structure below ground level is required, this should be in accordance with British Standard Code of Practice CP102:Part 1, and the Engineer should satisfy himself that the appropriate alternative therein mentioned is duly described in the Bill of Quantities or Drawings.

721. Painting
The manufacturers recommendations for the use of a paint system should always be checked to ensure it is suitable for application and use in the manner described.

SERIES 800 FENCES, MARKER AND INDICATOR POSTS

803. Permanent Fencing
1. This clause refers to the types of permanent fencing available to British Standard. It will nevertheless be necessary to give sufficient details in the Bill of Quantities to eliminate alternatives and ensure the Contractor has adequate data to price the type of fencing required.

Should the Engineer select a type of fence covered by the British Standards, but not defined in detail in the Specification, he will require to write additional clauses specifying his particular requirements.

804. Gates and Gate Posts
Under certain circumstances stiles over fences may be preferable to gates and their provision should not be overlooked. Their design is so much dependent on location and use as to preclude them from the Standard Specification.

807. Marker and Indicator Posts
These posts should be sited with care so as to avoid as far as possible obstructing grass cutting machinery on road verges and creating hazards at traffic circles and on pedestrian ways.

It is recommended that water authorities use blue nameplates with white letters and numerals for treated water only, and drainage authorities use white nameplates with the word 'Sewage', the appliance reference, for example 'A.V.' and numerals in black on sewage pressure pipelines.

SERIES 900 METAL STRUCTURES, CLADDING AND PAINTING

911-921 Painting
These clauses have been prepared for application to maintenance painting as well as the painting and protection of new construction work.

SERIES 1000 BIOLOGICAL FILTERS AND SLUDGE DRYING BEDS

General
The Specification has been written to suit orthodox types of biological filters and sludge drying beds. Where it is proposed to use proprietary types suitable additional clauses will require to be drafted for inclusion in the Specification.

SERIES 1100 ROADS, HARDSTANDINGS AND FOOTWAYS

General
The Specification is for substantial roads and parking areas and is not intended for minor access roads in remote areas to be used by light vehicles.

In general roads should be of sufficient width and junctions, particularly with public roads, of adequate horizontal curavature and sight line for their intended use.

SERIES 1200 MINOR ELECTRICAL INSTALLATIONS

General

This part of the Specification is intended to cover Minor Electrical Installations of a simple nature, where the Engineer responsible for the works considers the requirements can be met by the employment of a competent electrical contractor without reference to an Electrical Engineer. In this connection attention is drawn to the Roll of Contractors approved by the National Inspection Council for Electrical Installation Contracting, Trafalgar Buildings, 1 Charing Cross, London, SW1.

It is not intended to cover installations where these incorporate special requirements, sophisticated control systems or individual power units in excess of about 30 kilowatts on the basis that larger units associated with pumps etc. would be subject to a separate plant contract with specialist suppliers. It could, of course, be used in conjunction when meeting the simple standard requirements to 'service' installations of larger individual units supplied by specialist suppliers after any necessary amplification or adjustment.

It is intended to apply to lump sum tenders on a non-measurable basis except in respect of light fittings, small ancillary or portable units and the like, which would normally be covered by a Schedule.

Certain alternatives are offered in the Specification, e.g. steel conduit or plastic conduit and flush or surface mounting equipment. The Contract will require to define what is required in these and other cases where alternatives are given.

For supervision of testing, unless he is also qualified electrically, the Engineer should seek the assistance of an Electrical Engineer. It is suggested that, in certain circumstances, it may be possible to have this undertaken by a qualified inspector from the Employers' Insurers.

It is to be noted the Specification does not cover the installation of electrical equipment in situations where there could be an accumulation of explosive gas mixtures. In any such situations, the advice of an Electrical Engineer should be sought with reference to requirements of a flame-proof installation.

The Contract should also contain a schedule of cable sizes for all motor driven and other electrical equipment to be supplied by Contractors other than the Installation Contractor. If such a schedule is not included, the Contractor should be required to submit such a schedule with his tender so that the adequacy of his proposals in this respect may be checked.

SERIES 1300 TUNNELLING AND PIPEJACKING

General

This part of the Specification is intended for use with tunnels of up to 4 metres diameter. It should be read in conjunction with the safety documents, British Standards and other guidance notes highlighted within the text.

SERIES 1400 WATER MAINS RENOVATION

General

This specification relates only to cement mortar lining. For other techniques, such as slip lining, size-for-size replacement, epoxy resin lining and other proprietary systems, reference should be made to the Water Research Centre publication "Water Mains Rehabilitation Manual", 2nd Edition 1989 and specialist suppliers or contractors.

SERIES 1500 SEWER RENOVATION LINING

General

Further information on the design and performance of linings and sewer renovation techniques can be found in the WAA/WRc Sewerage Rehabilitation Manual.

The "Information and Guidance Notes" produced by WRc should be referred to where these are available for the types of lining chosen.

BED HAUNCH AND SURROUND TO PIPES

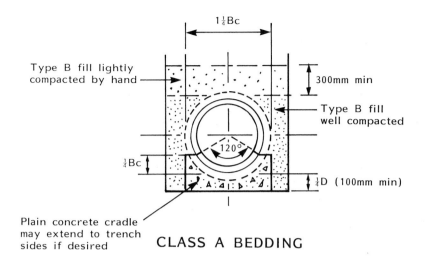

CLASS A BEDDING

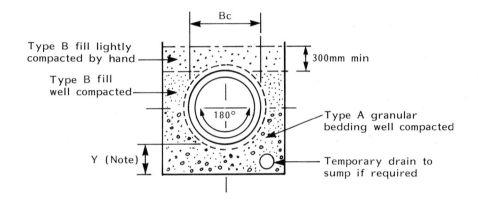

CLASS B BEDDING

Dimension Y

In rock or mixed soils containing rock bands, boulders, large flints or stones or other irregular hard spots, the depth of bed shall be $Y = \frac{1}{4}Bc$ or 150mm whichever is the greater, under the barrels but not less than 150mm under the sockets also. In uniform soils, the depth of bed shall be $Y = \frac{1}{6}Bc$ or 100mm whichever is the greater under the barrels but not less than 50mm under the sockets.

Bc Outside Diameter

D   Inside Diameter

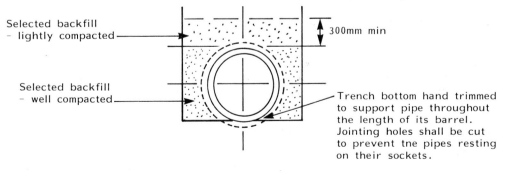

CLASS D BEDDING

BED HAUNCH AND SURROUND TO PIPES (CONTD.)

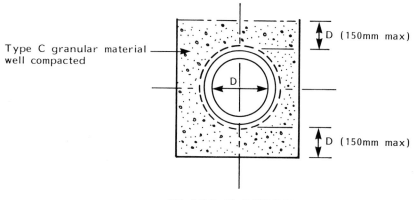

Type C granular material
well compacted

D (150mm max)

D

D (150mm max)

CLASS E BEDDING

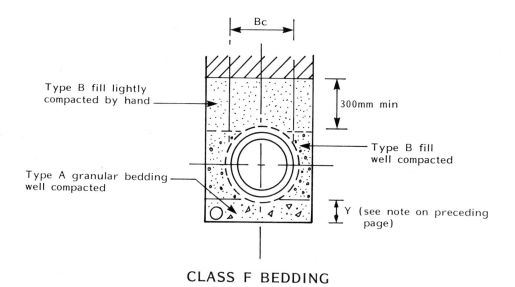

Bc

Type B fill lightly
compacted by hand

300mm min

Type B fill
well compacted

Type A granular bedding
well compacted

Y (see note on preceding
page)

CLASS F BEDDING

2 layers bituminous felt DPC
to Clause No. 315 or equal

Precast concrete or
engineering brick support

Fibreboard or equal

JOINT IN CONCRETE SUPPORT

BRICK MANHOLE LESS THAN 1.4m DEEP

TYPE A

Not to Scale

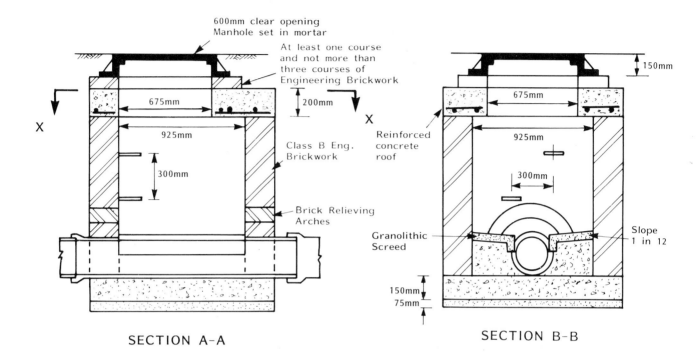

600mm clear opening
Manhole set in mortar

At least one course
and not more than
three courses of
Engineering Brickwork

200mm

675mm

925mm

300mm

Class B Eng.
Brickwork

Brick Relieving
Arches

SECTION A-A

150mm

675mm

925mm

300mm

Reinforced
concrete
roof

Granolithic
Screed

Slope
1 in 12

150mm
75mm

SECTION B-B

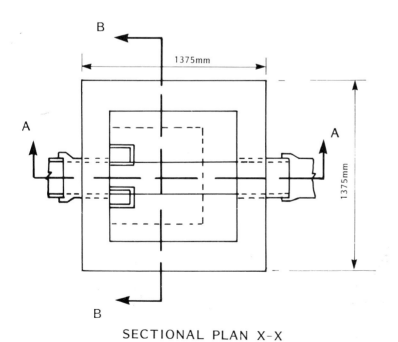

1375mm

1375mm

SECTIONAL PLAN X-X

BRICK MANHOLE 1.4m to 2.5m DEEP

TYPE B

Not to Scale

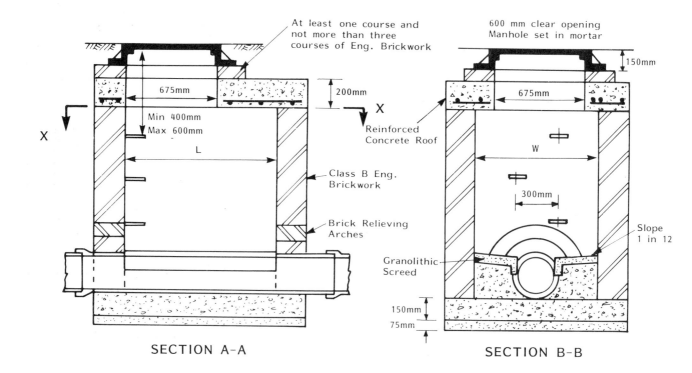

SECTION A-A

SECTION B-B

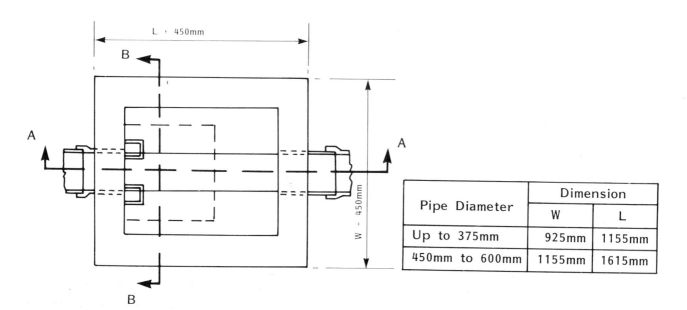

SECTIONAL PLAN X-X

Pipe Diameter	Dimension	
	W	L
Up to 375mm	925mm	1155mm
450mm to 600mm	1155mm	1615mm

BRICK MANHOLE 2.5m to 3.5m DEEP

TYPE C

Not to Scale

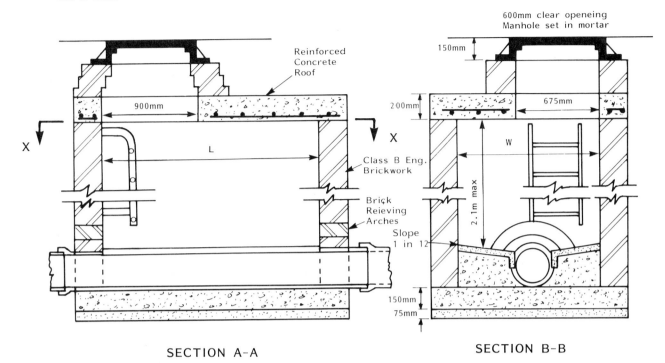

SECTION A-A

SECTION B-B

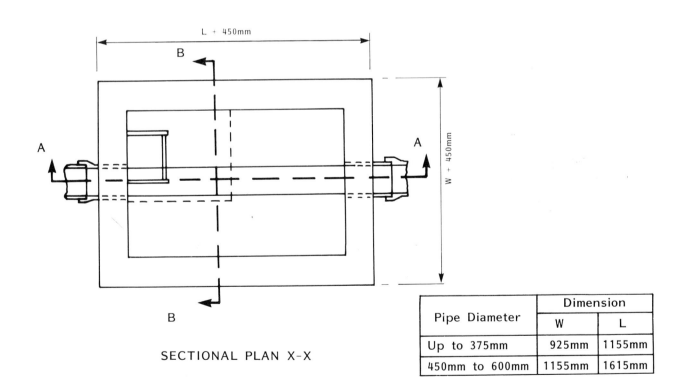

SECTIONAL PLAN X-X

Pipe Diameter	Dimension	
	W	L
Up to 375mm	925mm	1155mm
450mm to 600mm	1155mm	1615mm

153

PRECAST CONCRETE CIRCULAR MANHOLES – LESS THAN 4.5m DEEP

TYPE M

Not to Scale

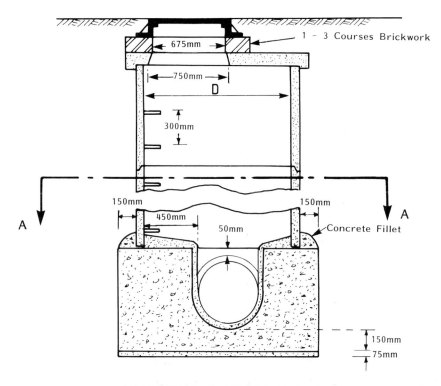

SECTIONAL ELEVATION ON B-B

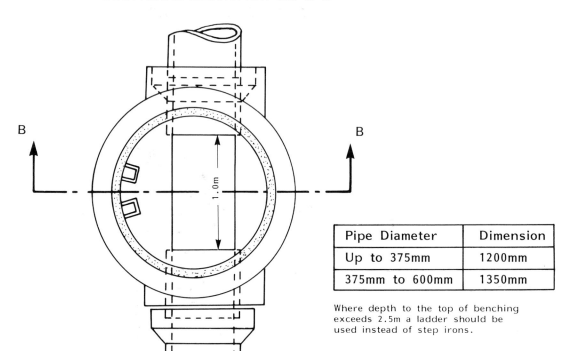

SECTIONAL PLAN ON A-A

Pipe Diameter	Dimension
Up to 375mm	1200mm
375mm to 600mm	1350mm

Where depth to the top of benching exceeds 2.5m a ladder should be used instead of step irons.

MANHOLE VALVE CHAMBER

TYPICAL DROP CONNECTION
BRICK OR CONCRETE MANHOLE

Not to Scale

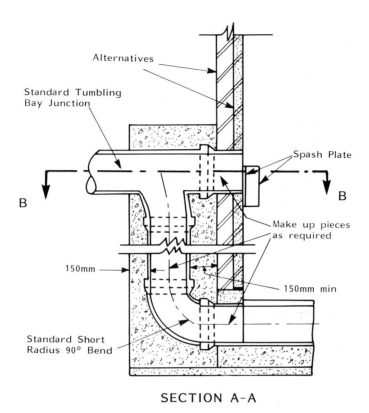

SECTION A-A

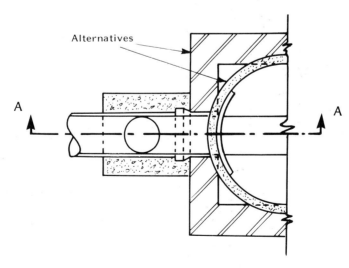

SECTION B-B

Check list of clauses which refer to matters requiring (or which may require) the Engineer to state his specific requirements in the Contract.

Series Clauses	100	Series Clauses	400	Series Clauses	600	Series Clauses	1200
	101.1		404.2		601.10		1205.1
	101.2		408.1		601.11		1205.2
	101.3		417.1		602.1		1205.3
	101.4		417.2		602.2		1205.7
	103.4		417.3		602.4		1208.2
	105.2		418.1		604.1		1209.1
	106.1		418.2		604.4		1210.1
	106.4		419.1		605.1		1210.3
	108.1		419.4				1210.4
	108.2		420.1	Series Clauses	700		1211.8
	108.4		420.3		715.2		1212.5
	111.1		420.6		717.1		1215.1
			420.7		728.1		1215.2
Series Clauses	200		421.1				
	201.3		421.6	Series Clauses	800	Series Clauses	1300
	201.4		423.2		801.2		1311.2
	202.2		425.1		802.2		1311.3
	205.3		426.4		807.2		1311.4
	207.1		429.2				1313.4
	208.1		431.1				1318.1
	209.1		431.4	Series Clauses	900		1323.2
	210.1		432.1		902.1		1324.6
	210.2		433.3		903.1		1325.1
	211.2		433.4		903.10		1325.3
	214.1		434.3		904.1		1325.4
	215.1		435.5		904.5		1326.1
	217.3		436.2		904.6		1326.3
	217.4		437.1		904.7		1326.4
	217.7		438.4		905.4		1327.4
	219.1		440.2		906.8		
	220.3		446.2		907.1	Series Clauses	1400
			446.3		908.1		1401.1
Series Clauses	300		446.6		908.2		1401.3
	303.1		446.7		909.1		1402.4
	304.4		448.1		910.2		1404.1
	305.1				914.2		1408.1
	305.2				915.3		1409.1
	305.3	Series Clauses	500		916.1		1410.1
	305.4		503.1		916.4		1411.1
	306.1		503.2		917.1		
	308.1		503.12				
	326.4		506.10	Series Clauses	1000		
	327.3		506.12		1005.1		
	328.2		506.16				
	332.1		509.4	Series Clauses	1100		
	332.4		512.2		1102.1		
	333.1		515.4		1109.3		
	336.2		515.5		1109.6		
	338.2		515.8		1109.7		
	346.3		517.2		1109.8		
	349.1		517.4		1109.12		
	352.1		517.5		1109.13		
	358.1		518.1		1109.14		
	365.1		519.3		1110.1		
	368.1		520.3		1110.3		
	372.1		523.5		1110.4		
	373.1		524.8				
	373.2		524.11				